£3.50

ian allan abc

**Miniature MR**

G000167974

## Robin Butterell, Dave Holroyde and Simon Townsend

**IAN ALLAN**
*Publishing*

No 1993 Pickie Puffer *in use on the 7¹/₄in gauge line at Pickie Fun Park, Bangor, Northern Ireland on 7 August 1996.*
Dave Holroyde

*The Mardyke 'Advanced Passenger Train' in action on the 7¹/₄in gauge Woodland Railway, 13 September 1994.*
Simon Townsend

*Various diverse influences are visible in the steam outline of this 4w-4PM running on the Queens Park Miniature Railway.*
Dave Holroyde

*Previous page: Zeus eases back into a departure road at Kingsmere, Moors Valley Railway.*

# CONTENTS

First published 1998

ISBN 0 7110 2593 2

Published by Ian Allan publishing an imprint of
Ian Allan Ltd, Terminal House, Station Approach, Shepperton, Surrey TW17 8AS.
Printed by Ian Allan Printing Ltd, Riverdene, Molesey Road, Hersham, Surrey KT12 4RG.

Code: 9804/B

# INTRODUCTION
## by Robin Butterell

In this book we have endeavoured to include details of all commercial miniature railways that will be open to the public during 1998, from 21in gauge down to 7¼in gauge.

Of course, all miniature railways are narrow gauge railways but the converse is not necessarily true. The best definition of a miniature railway is still that of a line on which the locomotives (and sometimes the rolling stock) are models of real or imaginary prototypes of larger or standard gauge types. Even so, some of the lines in this book are genuinely 'minimum gauge railways', doing jobs of work in their own right, without direct inspiration from larger ancestors.

In the early 1960s, researching into the number of lines open to the public, even including those with somewhat erratic opening times, I came up with a total of 50 of 15in gauge and under. These were made up of 11 of 15in gauge, 3 of 12in and 12¼in, 24 of 10¼in, 6 of 9½in and only 6 of 7¼in gauge. Included in the main part of this book are 167 miniature railways, 4 of over 15in gauge, 38 of 15in, 5 of 12¼ and 12in, 44 of 10¼, 6 of 8¼ to 9½in, and some 70 of 7¼in gauge.

Why has it been 23 years since the last book of this type was written (R. H. Leithead's *Miniature Railways Stockbook and Guide*, 1975)? Perhaps it is because of the challenge of keeping track of the whole miniature railway scene, which is forever changing.

I would like to thank all the miniature railway operators who contributed information for this book, and also my two co-authors. Dave Holroyde is Miniature Lines Records Officer for the Narrow Gauge Railway Society, and has provided most of the fact and figures that follow. Simon

Townsend is Editor of the Heywood Society Journal, and has been largely responsible for assembling it all into book form. I should also acknowledge the help of Peter Scott, whose book *Minor Railways* is published annually by the Branch Line Society.

Where photographs are not specifically credited, they were provided by the railways concerned. Dave Holroyde, Simon Townsend and I have taken every step we can to ensure accuracy of the information; any errors which may have occurred can be advised to us c/o the publisher.

The miniature railway, decades after the disappearance of main line steam, now occupies an important role in the overall scene for the railway enthusiast, with many superb and high quality layouts all over the United Kingdom to delight the discerning enthusiast and members of the general public.

*A double-header emerges from the tunnel at the Stapleford Miniature Railway, hauled by Nos 2943* Hampton Court *and 5565* Victoria, *on 25 August 1996. Dave Holroyde*

**Addresses:** These are in all cases the addresses of the railways concerned, rather than being postal addresses of the railways' operators. We have endeavoured to reflect county boundaries as at April 1996.

**Telephone numbers:** Where given, these are generally numbers of the location concerned. In a small number of cases the railway operators have permitted us to publish their home phone numbers these are marked (E). Please do not abuse these by calling at irregular hours.

**Operators:** Wherever known, these are the individuals or companies responsible for running trains, not necessarily the land or stock owners, or in the case of companies, the company owners.

**Line lengths:** These are approximate, to the nearest 50 yards.

**First opened:** These are the years of the first miniature railway presence on site, not necessarily of the same gauge or necessarily implying continuous service since.

**Locomotive numbers and names:**
These are shown as carried on the locomotives concerned; those not carried are denoted in brackets.

**Type:** *Steam:* The 'Whyte' notation of wheel arrangements has been used; ST: Saddle Tank; T: Side tank; VB: Vertical Boiler; WT: Well tank.

*Internal Combustion:* w indicates powered axle; for instance, 4-4w means two four wheeled bogies; rear bogie powered on all four wheels. 'Whyte' notation is used where transmission is by outside connecting rods, eg: 0-4-2DM. S/O: Steam outline; BE: Battery electric; DE: Diesel electric; DH: Diesel hydraulic; DM: Diesel mechanical: PM: Petrol mechanical; PH: Petrol hydraulic; RE: Electric, power from third rail.

**Builder:** Company names have been abbreviated e.g Severn Lamb Ltd to just Severn Lamb. In some cases, trading names have been used for individuals or partnerships.

**Opening hours:** We have not felt able to include detailed opening hours, which would have been lengthy and

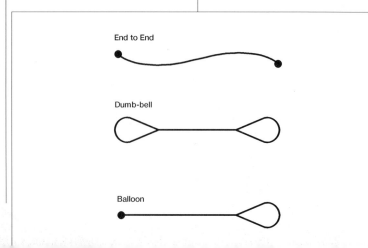

End to End

Dumb-bell

Balloon

subject to change. We have however included details where they are unusual, for instance one day a week. Some lines operate all year round, particularly those which are near to major centres of population rather than in seaside areas or amusement parks. Some railways only open weather permitting; one operator wrote this and then said, 'but it has to be pretty bad to stop us'; brave man! In virtually all cases, fine Sundays during the summer school holidays are the best times to find miniature railways busy.

**Photography and other matters:** Miniature lines offer much for the railway photographer; trains are frequent and there is immense variety between the different locations. Always start your visit by riding round on the train. It's the best way to see all the locations on offer, and to give something to the humble operator.

Always gain permission before crossing fences or entering the shed area. If the other locomotives are locked up, don't expect a guided tour in mid-afternoon; first thing or last thing are generally the best times.

Many operators of railways in this book are enthusiasts themselves to some extent, but the view from the footplate can be surprisingly different from that of the visitor. If you travel 150 miles on a wet Tuesday in June to find the railway deserted or the steam engine broken, don't blame us, we're just the authors. If on the other hand you have an enjoyable time, then mention *abc Miniature Railways* and say we sent you!

**Disclaimer:** The information contained in this publication has been published in good faith and every effort has been made to ensure its accuracy. Neither the publisher nor the authors can accept any responsibility for any error or misinterpretation. All liability for loss, disappointment, negligence or other damage caused by reliance on the information contained in this publication, or in the event of any bankruptcy or liquidation or cessation of the trade of any company, individual or firm mentioned is hereby excluded.

*Passengers admire 4-8-4* Queen of Nebraska *as she fills up with water, on the Union Pacific Railroad at Dobwalls.*
Robin Butterell

Models have been made by man from time immemorial, either to show how an object would look when constructed, or for the fascination and satisfaction of showing the object in a smaller scale when complete. With the advent of railways and the steam locomotive in the nineteenth century, models were produced which fell into both these categories. The manufacturer would produce models to illustrate the finished article to their clients, and the enthusiast (initially) would produce models of his favourite engine for his own satisfaction. Sometimes these were put to practical purposes with tracks to run on, and before long manufacturers began to exploit this new trade. It was only a matter of time before the more ambitious protagonists produced locomotives and rolling stock of such a size that the driver could sit on the locomotive (or tender) and pull coaches carrying real passengers.

Alongside these model builders there came Sir Arthur Percival Heywood. Sir Arthur believed that railways as small as 15in gauge could perform a useful job of work. He built his first locomotive in 1875, and with it a spectacular railway which, literally, climbed up the hill behind his house at Duffield in Derbyshire. Publication of his book *Minimum Gauge Railways* led in 1896 to the construction of a second, longer, railway for the Duke of Westminster at Eaton Hall in Cheshire. Other than this one could say that Sir Arthur's ideas never really caught on in his lifetime, but today his name is revered as the founder of small railways designed in their own right rather than as models.

It was the Cagney Brothers in the USA who first exploited the notion of

small railways as pleasure attractions. When a few of their train sets arrived over here, they led W. J. Bassett Lowke and Henry Greenly to think that they too could build miniature railways. Bassett Lowke was an astute businessman who came to be doyen of the model railway world; Greenly was a brilliant designer whose legacy may still be seen at many of the locations in this book.

In 1905 Bassett Lowke's works at Northampton built a 15in gauge 4-4-2, of broadly scale appearance, for passenger hauling which they tested on the Eaton Hall Railway. A full day's running produced some impressive results, including a top speed of 26mph with a 2 ton load behind. The locomotive, named *Little Giant*, was the first of a series of four 15in gauge Greenly designs, each one being bigger than the last. These engines were built and operated at locations in this country and on the Continent at exhibitions in pleasure parks.

During the 1900s Greenly advocated to the Society of Model and Experimental Engineers three standard miniature railway gauges, $7\frac{1}{4}$in gauge ($1\frac{1}{2}$in to the foot scale), $9\frac{1}{2}$in gauge (2in to the foot scale) and 15in gauge. By 1910 Bassett Lowke could supply equipment in all three scales, designed by Greenly. Whatever the customer wanted, from castings and drawings to complete railways, they continued to sell right up to 1939. For the larger garden or small estate $7\frac{1}{4}$in gauge was the obvious answer; by the 1920s Louis Shaw was already running his $7\frac{1}{4}$in gauge locomotives on public railways. During the 1930s J. C. Jeffress built a notable $7\frac{1}{4}$in railway at Kenton on which open days would occasionally be held.

9½in gauge was never as popular, because by 1910 the virtues of 10¼in gauge had already been proven and well publicised. The first 10¼in gauge railway had been built by J. A. Holder in Birmingham from beginnings around 1893, with improvements leading to a comprehensive private railway system by 1902. In 1904 Holder married and moved to Broome, near Stourbridge, where a still more ambitious line was built. In 1928 he moved again, this time to Keeping House, near Beaulieu, where a further railway was set up. Much of Holder's railway equipment survives today, albeit mostly in private hands.

Bassett Lowke's most ambitious venture was to take over an abandoned 3ft gauge line on the Cumbrian coast at Ravenglass, and re-lay the 7-mile track to 15in gauge. Here a mixture of scale locomotives and minimum gauge types from the estate of the late Sir Arthur Heywood were put to work. The Ravenglass and Eskdale Railway, as it was known, opened in 1915, in spite of the war. It operated continuously, augmented by a thriving granite traffic on a gauntleted 4ft 8½in line until taken over by a preservation society in 1960, from when it has gone from strength to strength. Bassett Lowke's company, Narrow Gauge Railways Ltd, also built the 15in gauge Fairbourne Railway, which led a quiet existence up to 1939.

Henry Greenly's ultimate achievement came in 1927 with the design of the Romney Hythe and Dymchurch Railway. Conceived by its owner, Jack Howey, as a main line in miniature, in due course it stretched for 14 miles along the low-lying Romney marshes in Kent from Hythe to Dungeness, a shingle promontory which juts out into the English Channel. Here the locomotives were modelled on London & North Eastern Railway Pacifics, but to ⅓ scale, giving an impressive appearance. They are all still operating today, some 70 years on.

The final prewar development that deserves mention is the Surrey Border & Camberley railway, which remains the most ambitious 10¼in gauge railway ever built. Like the RH&DR it arose through the meeting of a brilliant engineer, H. C. S. Bullock, and a wealthy enthusiast, Alexander Kinloch. Bullock got his inspiration from having met Captain Holder at Keeping House, and built in a short time a series of locomotives with obvious GWR influence, but very powerful and rugged. Kinloch took over a line started by Bullock which outgrew itself and was rebuilt as the SB&CR, running from Farnborough to Camberley. A five-platform terminus was built, anticipating all the traffic that would flock to a leisure attraction linking two main roads in the heart of the commuter belt. The well-publicised opening in 1938 was by Graham Moffatt, who achieved fame as the 'fat boy' in Will Hay's film *Oh! Mr Porter*. Alas the economics of such a grandiose scheme were seriously flawed, and the outfit was well on the way to bankruptcy when war intervened.

With the return to normal conditions in 1945, people began to reactivate the leisure situation and miniature railways, some of which had been 'mothballed' for the duration were opened up again, and a considerable number of new lines were built. With them came a new generation of designers and builders, such as Trevor Guest, David Curwen, John Thurston and Ernest Dove. Trevor Guest had entered the world of miniature railways when, with a partner, he built two very practical 10¼in gauge Atlantics in 1937/8. In 1938 their railway was set up at Dudley Zoo, where it proved very popular. In 1946 the line was regauged to 15in, and over the next 20 years Guest's company (G&SLE) built a series of sturdy locomotives for Dudley Zoo, Fairbourne and other railways. These included the two handsome minimum gauge 2-4-2s *Katie* and *Sian*, which were designed by Ernest Twining, another notable character who had worked with and for Bassett Lowke.

David Curwen was asked in 1946 to build a 10¼in gauge locomotive, which he based on an 'LBSC' design, in the style of an LNER Pacific. It is always more economic to build two locomotives, obtaining castings and other components for both simultaneously. A company was set up to run a second locomotive commercially, on a site at Weymouth. The 4-6-2 was quickly followed by a series of 4-4-2s of broadly USA outline, but built for practical operation, this being the Curwen hallmark. David was among the pioneers who in 1951 operated the Talyllyn Railway and thereby began the preservation movement. Thereafter he returned to his native Wiltshire where he has been designing and building miniature locomotives ever since, most recently for the 10¼in gauge railway at Audley End.

During the late 1960s David Curwen was introduced to Peter Lamb, whose company Severn Lamb Ltd was based at Stratford upon Avon. This led to a partnership whereby Severn Lamb built a number of larger miniature locomotives designed by David; the first of these was *Western Comet*, built in 1967, and still doing good service on the Brooklands Miniature Railway at Worthing. Subsequently the firm of Severn Lamb enjoyed a period of dominance in the market for heavily built railway equipment for the commercial railway operator. Steam outline i/c locomotives have been a particular speciality, and its 'Rio Grande' steam outline 2-8-0s and 2-6-0s operate, often unassisted, at many locations in this book. Now managed by Michael Severn Lamb, the company is still very much in business, but most recently its output has mostly been 2ft and 3ft gauge equipment for overseas amusement parks.

Two 7¼in gauge railways, the Greywood Central Railway and the Hilton Valley Railway, particularly paved the way for future developments. The Greywood Central was a complex private railway in the grounds of Sir John Samuel's house near Walton-on-Thames. Following Sir John's death the railway was, from 1965,

*Doyen of the miniature railway world, locomotive builder David Curwen in his workshop, with his 7¹/₄in gauge model of the Talyllyn Railway's 0-4-2ST Edward Thomas. Robin Butterell*

progressively re-established as the Great Cockcrow Railway near Chertsey. Here scale models of British standard gauge prototypes reign supreme, in an extremely intensive and professional operation. During the early days of the Great Cockcrow Railway, the Ian Allan Group extended its activities to miniature railway operation, building $10^{1}/_{4}$in gauge lines at seven locations, all powered by diesel locomotives.

The Hilton Valley Railway was located near Bridgnorth. From 1957 its owner Michael Lloyd opened the railway on Sunday afternoons, with takings going to charity. In Hilton's easy-going atmosphere, developments moved far beyond the concepts of 'scale', with some very heavy and durable stock and locomotives being built. The HVR closed in 1979, following the death of Michael Lloyd.

In 1968 Roger Marsh designed and built *Tinkerbell*, an $7^{1}/_{4}$in 0-4-2T which the driver sits in rather than on. A batch of these were built at his Hinckley works, and were followed by a series of 0-4-0ST 4in scale Hunslet quarry engines, and then *Romulus*, an 0-4-0WT designed to be easy enough for the home builder. The Hunslet was taken over and improved by Milner Engineering, who offered it as a complete locomotive or parts for the model engineer, along with other standard types. Castings for all these designs are still being sold. Other major constructors worth noting were Coleby Simkins and TMA Engineering.

In 1973 the $7^{1}/_{4}$in Gauge Society was founded. Up to this point most model engineers had built locomotives usually in $2^{1}/_{2}$in, $3^{1}/_{2}$in or 5in gauge, which really require elevated tracks in order to be run safely. Although there are 5in gauge lines laid on the ground, they are mainly for private operation where the passengers realise the need to sit up very straight so as not to disturb the centre of gravity! Then it

was realised that a $7^{1}/_{4}$in gauge railway can be built for not that much more than 5in gauge. The stock is all a bit heavier but you don't need an elevated track. Equally some enthusiasts who built $7^{1}/_{4}$in gauge lines for their own pleasure found that they naturally attracted visitors, and with a bit of extra effort could be opened to the public commercially. The Forest Railway at Dobwalls started this way, among the first of many in this book.

Growth in $7^{1}/_{4}$in gauge was also helped by the emergence of suppliers such as Cromar White and Mardyke Miniature Railways. Cromar White's strength was that they could supply and build complete railways for the private or commercial customer, $7^{1}/_{4}$in or $10^{1}/_{4}$in gauge, everything from the initial site survey onwards. Their track, aluminium alloy rail with closely spaced wooden sleepers, still does good service all over the country. Mardyke found particular success supplying the smaller end of the commercial railway market. Their speciality was a range of sit-in diesel and petrol locos, all with scale model outlines and very simple and robust hydrostatic drives; push the lever forward and you're off. Other innovations included tilting carriages, and pressed steel 'Supatrak', akin to Hornby Tinplate but on $7^{1}/_{4}$in gauge. Again, the number of Mardyke locomotives still operating speaks for itself. Pfeifferbahn, and more recently Roger Greatrex, have also made major contributions to the $7^{1}/_{4}$in gauge market.

You could say that the 'minimum gauge' concept was originally 15in, was taken over by $7^{1}/_{4}$in, and has now spread to sizes in between. The Mull Railway and the Bickington Steam Railway are prominent among $10^{1}/_{4}$in lines with 'small' rather than 'scale' profiles. Here both passengers and driver sit inside the trains. $10^{1}/_{4}$in gauge passenger-carrying vehicles strike a balance between width and stability. Some of them can seat two adults side by side, but sometimes you get to know your neighbour well. Most 7¼in gauge passenger vehicles are 'sit astride' types, which have high capacity for a given weight. Some of the latest 15in gauge vehicles seat three side by side.

John Ellerton found another permutation when he commissioned four half-size 2ft gauge locomotives for 12¼in gauge, these now run at Fairbourne. 12¼in gauge is less than 350mm, above which gauge lines fall within the official remit of Health & Safety Executive's Railway Inspectorate. The Exmoor Steam Railway has been a notable follower in 12¼in gauge. The most recent locomotives built there (both for themselves and for customers such as the 15in gauge lines at Perrygrove and Markeaton Park) further blur the distinctions between 'miniature' and 'narrow gauge' designs, as though one of the well-known narrow gauge locomotive builders from the past, such as Hunslet or Kerr Stuart, had decided

not to stop at 2ft, or even in some cases 18in gauge, and carried on down to smaller gauges.

By visiting a balanced selection of say 10 or 20 miniature railways you can expect to see strands of history from most of the developments above. There are enthusiasts sharing their hobby by running public trains hauled by scale models. There are those continually exploring the concept of 'minimum gauge', and amusement park operators who just want trains that are economic to run and look OK to a six year old. There are 'basic' lines, and others that have gone to great trouble building lineside accessories, such as signals, level crossings, platforms, station buildings. There are lines opened 50 or 80 years ago, and others that are brand-new; and an equally colourful mix of locomotives. It's a fascinating world, which we hope this book will encourage you to explore.

*Thomas II* takes its train over a diamond crossing at Mount Delight on the Beer Heights Light Railway. Robin Butterell

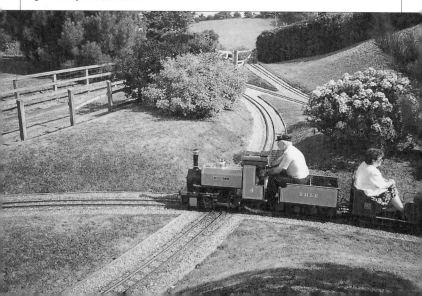

## BEER HEIGHTS LIGHT RAILWAY  *7¹/₄in gauge*

Pecorama, Underlys, Beer, nr Seaton, Devon EX12 3NA
Telephone: 01297 21542   OS Ref: SY224893   Operator: Howe & Davis Ltd
Line length: 1,300yd, complex   First opened: 1975

| No | Name | Type | Builder | Built |
|----|------|------|---------|-------|
| 3 | *Dickie* | 0-4-2 | D. Curwen | 1976 |
| 4 | *Thomas II* | 0-4-2ST | R. Marsh | 1979 |
| 5 | *Linda* | 2-4-0ST | J. Clarke | 1971 |
| 6 | *Jimmy* | 4-4wDH | Severn Lamb | 1986 |
| 7 | *Mr P* | 2-4-2 | BHLR | 1997 |

This line is built high on a hill with deep cuttings, high embankments and a long tunnel under the car park. Immaculately maintained with full signalling and realistic lineside buildings, the railway is one of the finest in the country. Pecorama is closed on Saturday afternoons, except on bank holiday weekends. An 0-6-0T is under construction.

## BICKINGTON STEAM RAILWAY  *10¹/₄in gauge*

Trago Mills Shopping & Leisure Centre, Stover, Nr Newton Abbot, Devon TQ12 6JB
Telephone: 01626 821111   OS Ref: SX821742   Operator: Trago Mills
Line length: 1¹/₄ miles   First opened: 1988

| No | Name | Type | Builder | Built |
|----|------|------|---------|-------|
| 750 | *Blanche of Lancaster* | 4-4-2 | D. Curwen | 1948 |
| 1 | *E. R. Calthrop* | 2-6-4T | Coleby Simkins | 1974 |
|  | *Alice* | 2-6-0 | Simkins & Vere | 1984 |
| 24 | *(Sandy River)* | 2-6-2 | Clarkson/Vere & Nicholson | 1991 |
| D5905 | *IXL* | 4w-4wDH | D. Nicholson | 1987 |

This line has an imposing main station at Trago Central, from where trains descend over a 23 pier viaduct, before looping round across themselves several times and then climbing back again. At one point there are six parallel tracks all on different levels. Up to four trains can run at once, controlled by computerised signalling. *E. R. Calthrop* is a model of a 2ft 6in gauge loco which once ran on the Leek & Manifold Railway in Staffordshire. *Blanche of Lancaster* once achieved fame by appearing on TV in an episode of *The Avengers*, filmed at the Stapleford Miniature Railway.

No 24 *being prepared to haul another train from Trago Central station, Bickington Steam Railway.* Robin Butterell

## BLAISE CASTLE MINIATURE RAILWAY *15in gauge*

Blaise Castle, Henbury, Bristol BS10 7QS
Telephone (E): 01275 872670   OS Ref: ST559786   Operators: A & R Giles
Line length: 350yd, end to end   First opened: 1974

| No | Name | Type | Builder | Built |
|----|------|------|---------|-------|
| 1 | *Vincent* | 2w-2-4BER | Hayne/Minirail | 1983 |
| 2 | *Goram* | 2w-2-4BER | Hayne/Minirail | 1977 |

A charming if idiosyncratic line, popular with children visiting the Blaise Castle estate. Both railcars were originally coaches, much modified by Norman Hayne (the line's previous owner) using milk float technology to provide traction. They are now named after giants who, as legend has it, once roamed the estate.

Vincent, *a battery electric railcar, on the Blaise Castle Miniature Railway.*
Simon Townsend

## BREAN CENTRAL MINIATURE RAILWAY *7¹/₄in gauge*

Brean Leisure Park,  Coast Road, Brean, Somerset  TA8 2RF
Telephone: 01278 751595   OS Ref: ST296544   Operator: J. Colishaw
Line length: 250yd, circular   First opened: 1973

| No | Name | Type | Builder | Built |
|------|------|------|---------|-------|
| 6691 | | 4-4wPH | R. Greatrex | 1986 |

A short line encircling this small amusement park, passing through the tunnel/shed as it goes.

## BUCKFASTLEIGH MINIATURE RAILWAY *7¹/₄in gauge*

South Devon Railway Station, Buckfastleigh, Devon  TQ11 0DZ
OS Ref: SX747663   Operator: G. Cooper   Line length: 600yd, circular
First opened: 1977

| No | Name | Type | Builder | Built |
|----|------|------|---------|-------|
| | *Romulus* | 0-4-0 | Corder/Cooper | 1998 |
| | *Bob* | 0-6-0PH | G. Cooper | 1995 |
| | | 0-4-0ST | R. Vaughton | |

This railway runs around the picnic area behind the locomotive shed at the South Devon Railway. Several lines here have come and gone before this one; 2-6-2T *Yeo* operated here before moving on when the Gorse Blossom Miniature Railway Park opened.

## CLEVEDON MINIATURE RAILWAY  9¹/₂in gauge

Salthouse Fields, Clevedon, North Somerset BS21 7XP
Telephone (E): 01275 872670   OS Ref: ST398710   Operator: A. Giles
Line length: 500yd   First opened: 1952

| No | Name | Type | Builder | Built |
|----|------|------|---------|-------|
| 595 | *Charles Henry* | SO 2-8-0PH | Severn Lamb | 1976 |

This locomotive is the smallest gauge of Severn Lamb 'Rio Grande' yet built, No 595 was its owner's number before his retirement from the police service. The circuit runs around an open field; steam once operated here many years ago.

No 595 Charles Henry *at the head of a train at the Clevedon Miniature Railway, in June 1995.*

## COMBE MARTIN WILDLIFE PARK RAILWAY  15in gauge

Combe Martin Wildlife Park, Higher Leigh Manor, Combe Martin, Devon
Telephone: 01271 882486   OS Ref: SS600452   Operator: Mr Butcher
Line length: 500yd, end to end   First opened: 1989   Park entry fee

| No | Name | Type | Builder | Built |
|----|------|------|---------|-------|
|  |  | S/O 2-8-0PH | Severn Lamb | 1987 |

## CRICKET ST THOMAS RAILWAY  15in gauge

Cricket St Thomas Wildlife Park, nr Chard, Somerset TA20 4DD
Telephone: 01460 30755   OS Ref: ST376086   Operator: W. Taylor
Line length: 800yd, end to end   First opened: 1975   Park entry fee

| No | Name | Type | Builder | Built |
|----|------|------|---------|-------|
|  | *Saint Thomas* | 4w-4wDH | G&SLE | 1957 |
|  |  | S/O 0-6-2DH | Alan Keef | 1995 |

This line runs from Heavy Horse Halt, along the side of a valley and through animal enclosures, before swinging round over a substantial viaduct to terminate at Flamingo Junction.

# DOBWALLS FAMILY ADVENTURE PARK  *7¹/₄in gauge*

Dobwalls, Nr Liskeard, Cornwall PL14 6HD
Telephone: 01579 320325   OS Ref: SX213658   Operator: Forest Railways Ltd
Rio Grande Railroad: 1,300yd, circular   First opened: 1970
Union Pacific Railroad: 900yd, circular

| No | Name | Type | Builder | Built |
|----|------|------|---------|-------|
| 488 | *General Palmer* | 2-8-2 | D. Curwen | 1971 |
| 498 | *Otto Mears* | 2-8-2 | D. Curwen | 1980 |
| 818 | *Queen of Wyoming* | 4-8-4 | Severn Lamb | 1974 |
| 838 | *Queen of Nebraska* | 4-8-4 | Severn Lamb | 1981 |
| 8 | *David Curwen* | 2-6-2 | D. Curwen | 1972 |
| X4008 | *William Jeffers* | 4-8-8-4 | Severn Lamb | 1978 |
| 6908 | *Centennial* | 8w-8DH | Severn Lamb | 1979 |
| 3008 | *Mathias Baldwin* | 4w-4DH | Severn Lamb | 1980 |
| 248 | *Spirit of America* | 6-6+6w-6wDH | Severn Lamb | 1983 |
| 5908 | *Pioneer* | 6w-6wDH | Severn Lamb | 1989 |

'Circular' is techically correct but hardly does justice to the two routes of the Forest Railroads, which twist and climb around, under and over themselves, passing landmarks of their full sized counterparts as they go. *William Jeffers* is a model of the UP 'Big Boy' class, and really a sight in itself. If you haven't already been, you will find that these railroads have a high 'aah' factor. Recent practice has been to operate one route using steam and the other using diesel, on each day.

# EXMOOR STEAM RAILWAY  *12¹/₄in gauge*

Cape of Good Hope Farm, Bratton Fleming, Devon EX32 7SN
Telephone: 01598 710711   OS Ref: SS661382   Operators: T. Stirland & family
Line length: 1,100yd, end to end   First opened: 1990

| No | Name | Type | Builder | Built |
|----|------|------|---------|-------|
| 190 | *Yeo Valley* | 2-8-0T | Exmoor Steam Railway | 1990 |
| 191 | *Lorna Doone* | 0-6-0T | Exmoor Steam Railway | 1991 |
| 299 | *Denzil* | 0-4-2T | Exmoor Steam Railway | 1995 |

*A train traverses the spiral section at the Exmoor Steam Railway on 11 September 1994, headed by 0-6-0T Lorna Doone. Simon Townsend*

Since this location first opened to the public, developments and improvements have been made continually, the latest being the opening of a new terminus named Cape of Good Hope. Trains now run round here, before returning round the spiral section to Exmoor Central. This is very much a 'minimum gauge' railway; the Stirlands' expertise is such that they have supplied a number of steam locomotives for other lines. An 0-4-2T, 2-4-2T and a Meyer are under construction. Recently they have imported several 2ft gauge locos from South Africa, which are on static display here.

## EXMOUTH EXPRESS  *10¼in gauge*

Exmouth Fun Park, Marine Drive, Exmouth, Devon
OS Ref: SY003804   Line length: 150yd, circular   First opened: 1949

| No | Name | Type | Builder | Built |
|----|------|------|---------|-------|
|    |      | 4wDM | G. M. Kichenside | 1978 |

A short circuit forming part of the sea front amusements; the line passes through the stock shed *en route*.

## GORSE BLOSSOM MINIATURE RAILWAY & WOODLAND PARK
*7¼in gauge*

Gorse Blossom Farm, Liverton, Newton Abbot, Devon TQ12 6JD
Telephone: 01626 821361   OS Ref: SX815740   Operator: G. & P. Kichenside Ltd
Line length: 1,500yd, circular   First opened: 1984

| No | Name | Type | Builder | Built |
|-----|---------|---------|---------------------|-------|
|     | *Yeo* | 2-6-2T | Milner Engineering | 1979 |
| 615 | *Klosters* | 4w-4wBE | Pfeifferbahn | 1990 |
|     | *Pegasus* | 4-4wBE | W. Baker | *c*1982 |
| 2   | *Heidi* | 4wBE | Cromar White | 1976 |

Yeo *hauls her train out of the station, at the Gorse Blossom Miniature Railway.*
Robin Butterell

*Yeo* and *Klosters* take their passengers for a ride in and out of the woodlands through tunnels and over a girder bridge; not easy to work out where you're going next. There is also a separate double track circuit 100yd long, around which visitors can drive the two smaller locos themselves. This encircles an ambitious 'G scale' railway based on the Rhaetian Railway main line between Solis and Preda. Trains to ride on, trains to look at, and a train you can drive yourself.

## HUNTERS REST MINIATURE RAILWAY *7¹/₄in Gauge*

Hunters Rest Public House, King Lane, Clutton Hill, nr Temple Cloud, Bath &
North East Somerset BS18 4QL
Telephone: 01761 452303   OS Ref: ST633601   Operator: M. Pearce
Line length: 400yd, circular   First opened: 1984

| No | Name | Type | Builder | Built |
|----|------|------|---------|-------|
| | *Taurus* | 4w-4PH | Mardyke | *c*1983 |
| | *Half Pint* | 0-4-0ST | J. Woodroofe | *c*1985 |

A steeply graded layout at the back of this public house, including a double track station and tunnel. The line runs through deep cuttings around Blackberry Hill and adjacent to the small lake.

## JUNGLE EXPRESS *10¹/₄in gauge*

Paignton Zoological and Botanical Gardens, Totnes Road, Paignton,
Devon TQ4 7EU
Telephone: 01803 697500   OS Ref: SX878576   Operator: Whitley Wildlife
Conservation Trust   Line length: 500yd, circular   First opened: 1937
Zoo entry fee

| No | Name | Type | Builder | Built |
|----|------|------|---------|-------|
| | *Marie* | 4-4wPM | G&SLE | 1939 |
| 37401 | | 4w-4wDH | Nicholson/Wedgewood | 1995 |

This long-established line runs around a lake and through the stock shed/tunnel at the back of the circuit.

*No 37401 ready to depart with a full train at Paignton Zoo.* Robin Butterell

## LAPPA VALLEY STEAM RAILWAY  *15in, and also 7¹/₄in & 10¹/₄in gauges*

St Newlyn East, Newquay, Cornwall TR8 5HZ
Telephone: 01872 510317   OS Ref: SW839573
Operator: Lappa Valley Rly Co Ltd
15in gauge: 1¹/₄miles, end to end;   First opened: 1974
Newlyn Branch line; 10¹/₄in gauge: 750yd, balloon   First opened: 1995
Woodland Railway; 7¹/₄in gauge: 300yd, circular   First opened: 1978

| No | Name | Type | Builder | Built |
|---|---|---|---|---|
| *15in gauge* | | | | |
| No 1 | *Zebedee* | 0-6-4T | Severn Lamb | 1974 |
| No 2 | *Muffin* | 0-6-0 | Berwyn Engineering | 1967 |
| No 3 | *Gladiator* | 4w-4DH | Minirail | 1960 |
| No 4 | *Pooh* | 4wDM | Lister | 1942 |
| *10¹/₄in gauge* | | | | |
| | *Duke of Cornwall* | 4w-4PH | Severn Lamb | 1981 |
| | | 4-4wPMR | N. Tambling | 1995 |
| *7¹/₄in gauge* | | | | |
| | | 4w+4wPH | Mardyke | 1987 |

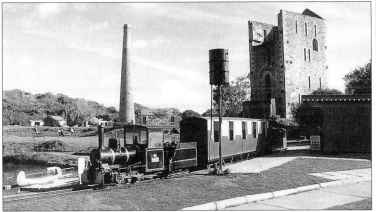

*Muffin and train awaiting passengers at East Wheal Rose, Lappa Valley Railway, in October 1995.* Keith J. Lloyd

This is the only location in this book where you can ride upon three different gauges of miniature railway. The 15in gauge takes you from the car park at Benny Halt to East Wheal Rose, where there is a historic mine engine house, along with a boating lake and other attractions. From there, included in the one charge, you can travel further along the standard gauge trackbed using the 10¹/₄in gauge line, or with the kiddies whizz round in circles in a sit in 'APT' set on the 7¹/₄in gauge. Founded by Eric Booth, this popular attraction is now owned and operated by his family. Watch out for some interesting technical features, like the cross between a turntable and a sector plate at Benny Halt.

## LITTLE WESTERN RAILWAY  *7¹/₄in gauge*

Trenance Gardens, Newquay, Cornwall
Telephone: 01872 510317   OS Ref: SW819614   Operator: E. Booth
Line length: 300yd, circular   First opened: c1965

| No | Name | Type | Builder | Built |
|----|------|------|---------|-------|
|  |  | 4-4wPH | Mardyke | 1980 |
| 7135 |  | 4-4wPH | Mardyke | 1983 |

This attractive little line is normally operated by a Mardyke 'HST' set, but a Lilliput 'Royal Scot' of 1954 appears occasionally; contact the Lappa Valley Railway for details.

## LONGLEAT RAILWAY   *15in gauge*

Longleat House, Warminster, Wiltshire BA12 7NW
Telephone: 01985 844400   OS Ref: ST808432   Operator: J. Hayton
Line length: 1¹/₄ miles, balloon   First opened: 1965   Park entry fee

| No | Name | Type | Builder | Built |
|----|------|------|---------|-------|
| 3 | *Dougal* | 0-6-2T | Severn Lamb | 1970 |
| 5 | *Ceawlin* | S/O 2-8-2DH | Severn Lamb/Hayton | 1975 |
| 4 | *Lenka* | 4+4wDHR | Hayton | 1984 |

Situated adjoining the well-known stately home of Lord Bath, the line runs from Longleat Central station through parkland and alongside a lake for half a mile, where sea lions and monkeys can be seen on an island. Hippos sometimes surface. A busy, well-established line.

*Dougal* stands by the water tank at Longleat.  Robin Butterell

## MOORS VALLEY RAILWAY  *7¹/₄in gauge*

Moors Valley Country Park, Horton Road, Ashley Heath, nr Ringwood, Dorset BH24 2ET
Telephone: 01425 471415   OS Ref: SU104060   Operator: Narogauge Ltd
Line length: 2,000yd   First opened: 1986

| No | Name | Type | Builder | Built |
|----|------|------|---------|-------|
| 1 | *Sir Goss* | 2-4-0 | J. Goss | 1981 |
| 3 | *Talos* | 0-4-2T | R. Marsh | 1978 |
| 4 | *Tinkerbell* | 0-4-2T | R. Marsh | 1968 |
| 5 | *Sapper* | 4-6-0 | R. Marsh/J. Haylock | 1982 |
| 6 | *Medea* | 2-6-2T | J. Haylock/M. Sharp/J. Goss | 1981 |
| 7 | *Aelfred* | 2-6-4T | Tuckton | 1985 |
| 9 | *Jason* | 2-4-4T | Moors Valley Railway | 1989 |
| 10 | *Offa* | 2-6-2 | Moors Valley Railway | 1991 |
| 11 | *Zeus* | 2-6-2 | A. Culver/Moors Valley Rly | 1991 |
| 12 | *Pioneer* | 4-6-2 | Moors Valley Railway | 1992 |
| 13 | *Tiny Tim* | 0-4-0T | Moors Valley Railway | 1993 |
| 14 | *Horton* | 2-4-0 | Moors Valley Railway | 1991 |
| 15 | *William Rufus* | 2-4-0+0-4-2T | Moors Valley Railway | 1996 |

*The 'minimum gauge' philosophy on 7¹/₄in gauge is well illustrated by this photograph of 0-4-2T* Talos *heading a goods train on the Moors Valley Railway.*

Conceived as a small gauge railway capable of carrying 150,000 passengers per year, the Moors Valley is really in a class of its own. It all started when Roger Marsh built *Tinkerbell*, which was the first 7¹/₄in gauge locomotive one sat in, rather than on. From this basic theme Jim Haylock has developed the railway's impressive stud of minimum gauge locomotives, capable of hauling heavy trains around the steep gradients and sharp curves of this line, particularly where it spirals around the adventure playground.

When the railway moved here from Tucktonia in 1985, what is now Kingsmere station was the hub of a dairy farm. Now the buildings form a four-platform enclosed station, carriage shed, workshop, locomotive shed and shop. Movements are controlled from two signalboxes, that at Kingsmere having the lever frame formerly installed at Beckton Gas Works in East London. Although basically a circuit, passengers normally travel over the line in two journeys, detraining at Kingsmere whilst the train draws into the headshunt and then back into a departure road. On Sundays only throughout the year a special train, the 'Midday Limited' departs for a non-stop run (signals permitting) twice around the circuit, once in each direction. On peak days there is also a shuttle train between Lakeside and Kingsmere stations. Regular special events are held.

It might be $7\frac{1}{4}$in gauge, but the Moors Valley is a complete railway in every sense.

## PARADISE RAILWAY   *15in gauge*

Paradise Park, Hayle, Cornwall TR27 4HY
Telephone: 01736 753365   OS Ref: SW555365   Operator: Paradise Park
Line length: 250yd, circular   First opened: 1976   Park entry fee

| No | Name | Type | Builder | Built |
|------|---------|------|--------|------|
| No 3 | *Zebedee* | 4wDM | Lister | 1938 |

A short line in a corner of this bird park.

## PIXIELAND MINIATURE RAILWAY   *15in gauge*

Pixieland Fun Park, West St, Kilkhampton, nr Bude, Cornwall EX23 9QW
Telephone: 01288 321225   OS Ref: SS250114   Operator: D. Vanstone
Line length: 200yd, circular   First opened: 1980   Park entry fee

| No | Name | Type | Builder | Built |
|---|---------|--------|---------------------|------|
| 1 | *Pioneer* | 2-2wPM | K. Rosewell | 1947 |
| | *Dennis* | 0-4-2T | Exmoor Steam Railway | 1997 |

This line may seem short, but considering its location, cut into a steep hillside, it seems amazing that it was ever built in the first place. The little railway is an evergreen attraction among the childrens' rides at Pixieland, and has recently gained its own steam locomotive.

## POOLE PARK RAILWAY   *10¼in gauge*

Poole Park, Parkstone Road, Poole, Dorset
Telephone (E): 01202 683701   OS Ref: SZ025912   Operator: B Merrifield
Line length: 700yd, circular   First opened: 1949

| No | Name | Type | Builder | Built |
|----|------|------|---------|-------|
| D107 | | 4-6wPM | Southern Miniature Railways | c1958 |
| D7000 | *Desmond* | 4-6wDH | Southern Miniature Railways | c1964 |
| | *Arthur* | 0-6-0ST | J. Hudell | 1982 |

A long-established line meandering around the lake and through woodland in Poole Park. The steam loco is only used on certain Saturdays; best to check in advance (by telephone) if travelling a long distance to see it.

*The driver's concentration shows, as 0-6-0ST* Arthur *makes good speed on the Poole Park Miniature Railway.*

## RODE WOODLAND RAILWAY  *7¹/₄in gauge*

Rode Bird Gardens  Rode, Nr Bath, Somerset BA3 6QW
Telephone: 01373 830326   OS Ref: ST797546
Operators: D. Underhill & M. Marshall   Line length: 1,000yd, circular
First opened: 1988   Gardens entry fee

| No | Name | Type | Builder | Built |
|----|------|------|---------|-------|
| | *Yeoman Highlander* | 4w-4PM | Mardyke | c1981 |
| | *Sgt Murphy* | 0-6-0T | M. Marshall | 1990 |
| | *Earl Haig* | 0-6-0T | M. Marshall/D. Underhill | 1993 |

The 'Great Little Trains of Rode' wend their way from Woodland Central station through the trees and back again. A well-constructed line in a popular location. Special weekends are held with visiting locomotives during the year.

*Workings of* Earl Haig *are explained to a young enthusiast at Rode Woodland Railway, on 17 September 1994.* Simon Townsend

## SMOKEY OAK RAILWAY   *10¹/₄in gauge*

Woodland Park, Brokerswood, Westbury, Wiltshire BA13 4EH
Telephone: 01373 822238   OS Ref: ST838524   Operator: Woodland Park
Line length: 600yd, end to end   First opened: 1991   Park entry fee

| No | Name | Type | Builder | Built |
|----|------|------|---------|-------|
|    | *Amelia* | 4w-4wDH | Mardyke | 1987 |

The Woodland Park covers eighty acres of historic broad-leaved woodland, through part of which this line runs.

## TAMARISK MINIATURE RAILWAY   *7¹/₄in gauge*

Old Macdonald's Farm, Porthcothan Bay, nr Padstow, Cornwall
Telephone: 01841 540829   OS Ref: SW861711
Line length: 200yd, end to end   First opened: 1989

| No | Name | Type | Builder | Built |
|----|------|------|---------|-------|
| 1680 | *Komotion* | 4w-2PH | D. Burwell | 1986 |

## WESTON MINIATURE RAILWAY  *7¹/₄in gauge*

Beach Lawns, Marine Parade, Weston super Mare, North Somerset
Telephone : 01934 643510   OS Ref: ST316600   Operator: R. Bullock
Line length: 900yd, dumb-bell   First opened: 1981

| No | Name | Type | Builder | Built |
|----|------|------|---------|-------|
|    | *Petra* | 2-4-0 | G. White | 1989 |
| 1  |      | S/O 4wPH | R. Greatrex/R. Bullock | 1985 |
| 201 | *Hiawatha* | 4w-4PH | A. Bimpson | 1980 |

A popular line running round the putting green and then along the seafront at the southern end of Weston promenade. They also make a good cup of tea.

*At Weston Miniature Railway, WMR 1 stands next to Putters Junction signalbox.*

## WEYMOUTH BAY MINIATURE RAILWAY  *10¹/₄in gauge*

Lodmoor Country Park, Weymouth, Dorset DT4 7SX
Telephone: 01305 785747   OS Ref: SY685807
Line length: 500yd, circular   First opened: 1983

| No | Name | Type | Builder | Built |
|----|------|------|---------|-------|
|    |      | 4-4wPE | G. Hunt |      |
| 1890 |    | S/O 2-6-0DH | Severn Lamb | 1990 |

This line runs adjacent to some seaside amusements on the eastern outskirts of Weymouth.

## BRAMBRIDGE PARK GARDEN CENTRE RAILWAY  8¹/₄in gauge

Brambridge Park Garden Centre, Kiln Lane, Brambridge, Eastleigh, Hampshire
Telephone: 01962 713707   OS Ref: SU467222   Line length: 200yd, end to end
First opened: c1976

| No | Name | Type | Builder | Built |
|----|------|------|---------|-------|
| 815 | *Carolyn* | 2-6-2T | | 1925 |

Among public miniature railways this one is most unusual, featuring a raised track of 8¹/₄in gauge.

## BROOKLANDS MINIATURE RAILWAY   10¹/₄in gauge

Brooklands Pleasure Park, East Worthing, West Sussex
OS Ref: TQ173035   Operator: F Rainson   Line length: 1,000yd, circular
First opened: 1965

| No | Name | Type | Builder | Built |
|----|------|------|---------|-------|
| | *Western Comet* | 6-6wPH | Severn Lamb | 1967 |

This line runs round the boating pool at Brooklands, between Worthing and Lancing. A steam loco ran here for a short time; quite extensive earthworks were necessary to get the track onto a level course.

## CUCKOO HILL RAILWAY   7¹/₄in gauge

Avon Valley Nurseries, South Gorley, nr Ringwood, Hampshire
Telephone: 01425 653001   OS Ref: SU163105   Operator: R. Kinnison
Line length: 700yd, circular   First opened: 1991

| No | Name | Type | Builder | Built |
|----|------|------|---------|-------|
| | *Jupiter* | 2-4-0 | Moors Valley Railway | 1991 |

This line was built by the team from the Moors Valley Railway, and is operated during the fruit picking season.

## EASTBOURNE MINIATURE STEAM RAILWAY PARK   7¹/₄in gauge

Lottbridge Drove, Eastbourne BN23 6NS
Telephone: 01323 520229   OS Ref: TQ613012   Operators: M. & R. Wadey
Line length: 1,000yd, circular   First opened: 1992

| No | Name | Type | Builder | Built |
|-------|------|------|---------|-------|
| 1 | *Thomas* | 0-4-2T | M. Wadey | 1982 |
| 6172 | *Royal Green Jackets* | 4-6-0 | M. Wadey | 1988 |
| D7042 | *Eastbourne Herald* | 4w-4wPE | M. Wadey | 1987 |
| 4039 | *Rachel* | 0-6-0 | L. Markwick | 1993 |
| 3802 | | 2-8-0 | A. Newbery | 1988 |

*No 6172* Royal Green Jackets *on the turntable at Eastbourne Miniature Steam Railway, with Southbourne Lake visible in the background.* Dave Holroyde

Eastbourne's ⅛th scale miniature railway allows you to travel on replica coaches around Southbourne Lake; ideal for young and old alike. Railway style cafe and lineside nature trail; regular special events (including 'Friends of Thomas the Tank Engine') are held.

*The enduring attractions of 'Thomas the Tank Engine' stories are borne out by this busy scene during a 'Thomas' event at Eastleigh Lakeside Railway on 21 September 1996. The driver, railway owner Clive Upton, also looks happy.*

## EASTLEIGH LAKESIDE RAILWAY *7¼in gauge*

Lakeside Country Park, Wide Lane, Eastleigh, Hampshire
Telephone: 01703 636612   OS Ref: SU446175
Operator: Eastleigh Lakeside Railway Ltd.   Line length: 1,300yd, balloon
First opened: 1992

| No | Name | Type | Builder | Built |
|---|---|---|---|---|
| 4789 | *William Baker* | 4-4-2 | W. Baker | 1947 |
| 7 | *Sandy River* | 2-4-2 | A. Bimpson | 1983 |
| 1994 | *Eastleigh* | 0-4-0+0-4-0DH | M. Millard | 1994 |
| 1001 | *The Monarch* | 4-6-2 | H. Bullock | 1932 |
| 3 | *Francis Henry Lloyd* | 4-8-4 | Guest/Lloyd | 1959 |

Eastleigh Lakeside has recently joined the ranks of Britain's major miniature railways. Trains leave from Eastleigh Parkway station along the single line, through a passing loop, to a balloon loop. On the return journey they enter a turning wye before propelling back into the platform ready for the next departure. Periodic special events are held, including 'Thomas the Tank Engine' weekends, for which No 1001 is authorised to appear as No 4 *Gordon*.

## FAVERSHAM MINIATURE RAILWAY  *9in gauge*

Faversham Garden Centre, Teynham, nr Faversham, Kent
OS Ref: TQ970618
Line length: 300yd, end to end  First opened: 1995

| No | Name | Type | Builder | Built |
|---|---|---|---|---|
| No 2 | *Robin* | 4-4-0 | B. K. Field | 1935 |
| No 1 | *Bertie* | 4-4wBE | T. Smith | 1990 |
| D7043 | | 4w-4PM | Cromar White | *c*1974 |
| | | 4wPH | Iron Horse | 1990 |

This line takes its unusual gauge from a private miniature railway not far away, upon which the steam loco used to operate. Following a change in land ownership, the track is being relaid in a new direction to the back of the nursery. *Robin* is privately owned and makes occasional appearances here.

## GREAT COCKCROW RAILWAY  *7¼in gauge*

Hardwick Lane, Lyne, Chertsey, Surrey
Telephone: 01932 565474  OS Ref: TQ027662
Operator: Ian Allan Miniature Railway Supplies Ltd  Line length: 1 mile, complex
First opened: 1964

*On shed at the Great Cockcrow Railway, on the day of the opening of the branch line by Terence Cuneo.* Robin Butterell

A busy scene at Hardwick Central, Great Cockcrow Railway, with the 'Gladesman' preparing to depart double-headed.
Robin Butterell

| No | Name | Type | Builder | Built |
|---|---|---|---|---|
| 206 | | 2-6-0 | D. Simmonds | 1956 |
| 1947 | *Eureka* | 4-6-2 | L. Shaw | 1926 |
| 837 | | 4-6-0 | D. Curwen | 1948 |
| 6100 | *Royal Scot* | 4-6-0 | Barnett/Willoughby | 1948 |
| 1239 | | 4-4-0 | Baldwin Bros | 1912 |
| 1935 | | 2-6-0 | H. Saunders | 1975 |
| 11 | | 0-6-0PM | W. Jennings | 1959 |
| 7915 | *Mere Hall* | 4-6-0 | Rowe | 1952 |
| D7028 | *Alastair B. McLeod* | 4w-4wBE | A. Glaze | 1982 |
| 73755 | *Longmooor* | 2-10-0 | J. Liversage | 1948 |
| 6100 | *Royal Scot* | 4-6-0 | J. Butt | 1981 |
| 2403 | *Lorna Doone* | 4-6-2 | L. Shaw | 1936 |
| 5000 | *Sister Dora* | 4-6-0 | A. Glaze | 1981 |
| 70020 | *Mercury* | 4-6-2 | N. Sleet | 1985 |
| 1442 | | 4-4-2 | Parkinson/Hammond | 1988 |
| 850 | *Lord Nelson* | 4-6-0 | D. Scarrott | 1985 |
| 8200 | | 2-8-0 | D. Pownall | c1983 |
| 5145 | | 4-6-0 | Axon/Sleet | 1991 |
| 21C11 | *General Steam Navigation* | 4-6-2 | Lester/Sleet | 1993 |
| 8374 | | 2-8-0 | Glaze/Hancock | 1993 |
| 40106 | | 1Co-Co1PH | N. Sleet | 1992 |
| 4835 | | 4-6-0 | D. Benham | 1985 |
| 34051 | *Sir Winston Churchill* | 4-6-2 | N. Sleet | 1995 |
| 6115 | *Scots Guardsman* | 4-6-0 | P. Almond | 1988 |
| 70047 | *Lady of the Lake* | 4-6-2 | J. Butt | 1996 |
| 1401 | | 0-4-2T | R. Sills | 1980 |
| 1249 | *Hecate* | 0-8-0 | R. Sills | 1986 |

This is the inspirational home of $7^1/4$in (to the foot) scale railways in the UK. The above list represents a cross-section of locomotives likely to be on shed, but it's always changing. Trains from Hardwick Central generally operate over either the circuit route through Everglades Junction (several times, in different directions) or climb the hill over a 45ft viaduct to terminate at Cockcrow Hill. Periodically a double headed 'special' covers both routes; tickets may be booked in advance.

Most trains seat only 12 passengers but they run at very frequent intervals all afternoon. The intensive and highly professional operation is only made possible by strict block working between the two signalboxes. Authentic signalling is a particular feature, and the pace of events inside the boxes has to be seen to be believed.

The Great Cockcrow Railway is open on Sundays from May to October, from 2pm.

## HASTINGS MINIATURE RAILWAY   10¹/₄in gauge

Rock a Nore Road, Hastings, East Sussex
OS Ref: TQ828093   Line length: 600yd, end to end   First opened: 1948

| No | Name | Type | Builder | Built |
|----|------|------|---------|-------|
| | *Swee' Pea* | S/O 0-6-0DH | Alan Keef | 1990 |

This long-established line runs through the fishing area to the eastern end of Hastings seafront, not far from the East Hill cliff lift. Alas the three steam engines which once ran here are all now elsewhere. At least *Swee' Pea* has an attractive narrow gauge outline, and of course it represents 'instant power' for the commercial operator.

## HOLLYCOMBE STEAM COLLECTION   7¹/₄in gauge

Iron Hill, Midhurst Road, Liphook, Hampshire GU30 7LP
Telephone: 01428 724900   OS Ref: SU852295
Operator: Hollycombe Steam & Woodland Garden Society
Line length: 400yd, circular   First opened: 1982

| No | Name | Type | Builder | Built |
|----|------|------|---------|-------|
| | *(Bob)* | 0-4-2T | P. Howard | 1981 |
| | *Pauline* | 0-4-0 | M. Nicholls | c1989 |
| | | 4w-4PH | Mardyke | 1992 |
| | | 0-4-0 | Bennett Bros | 1990 |
| | | 0-6-0BE | | |

This small miniature line is an ancillary attraction at the magnificent Hollycombe collection, where one can also ride upon 2ft and standard gauge lines, besides being entertained by the Bioscope and steam fairground rides.

## LITTLEHAMPTON MINIATURE RAILWAY   12¹/₄in gauge

Mewsbrook Park, Littlehampton, West Sussex
OS Ref: TQ042016   Operator: C. Evans   Line length: 800yd, end to end
First opened: 1948

| No | Name | Type | Builder | Built |
|----|------|------|---------|-------|
| 28588 | *Southern Belle* | S/O 4-4wPH | Fontwell/Duggin | 1988 |

This long-established line runs from Norfolk Road, on the seafront, to Mewsbrook Park, a public park with boating rides etc. For many years the railway was operated by two 4-6-4s built by John Thurston, who thought up the 12¹/₄in gauge so as to give more stability than 10¹/₄in.

*No 28588 Southern Belle at Norfolk Road on the Littlehampton Miniature Railway.*
Dave Holroyde

## MARWELL'S WONDERFUL RAILWAY   *15in gauge*

Marwell Zoological Park, Colden Common, nr Winchester,
Hampshire SO21 1JH
Telephone: 01962 777407   OS Ref: SU508216
Operator: Marwell Preservation Trust   Line length: 900yd, dumb-bell
First opened: 1987   Zoo entry fee

| No | Name | Type | Builder | Built |
|----|------|------|---------|-------|
|    | *Princess Anne* | S/O 2-6-0DH | Severn Lamb | 1987 |

Marwell is world famous for its conservation and breeding of endangered species. The train ride gives close-up views of some of the animals.

## MERSTHAM VALLEY RAILWAY   *7¹/₄in gauge*

St Nicholas School, Taynton Drive, Merstham, nr Redhill, Surrey
OS Ref: TQ299525
Operator: St Nicholas School   Line length: 700yd, end to end
First opened: 1989

| No | Name | Type | Builder | Built |
|----|------|------|---------|-------|
|    | *Dippy* | 4wPH | G. Diplock | 1986 |
|    | *Duke of Warcaw* | 4w-4DER | J. Osborne | 1991 |
|    | *Topsy* | 4w-4wPHR | G. Diplock | 1988 |

A line around the playing fields of St Nicholas School.

## NEWHAVEN MINIATURE RAILWAY   *7¹/₄in gauge*

Paradise Family Leisure Park, Avis Road, Newhaven, East Sussex BN9 0DH
Telephone: 01273 512123   OS Ref: TQ448023
Operator: Paradise Family Leisure Park   Line length: 200yd, circular
First opened: 1989

| No | Name | Type | Builder | Built |
|----|------|------|---------|-------|
| D7068 | *Four Seasons* | 4w-4wDH | Mardyke | 1989 |

A simple circuit at the back of this garden/leisure centre. The 'Hymek' hauls a set of Mardyke 'sit in' coaches finished in 'Brighton Belle' colours.

## PAULTONS PARK RIO GRANDE MINIATURE RAILWAY  *15in gauge*

Paultons Park, Ower, Romsey, Hampshire SO51 6AL
Telephone: 01703 814442   OS Ref: SU317167   Operator: Paultons Park Ltd
Line length: 700yd, circular   First opened: 1987   Park entry fee

| No | Name | Type | Builder | Built |
|---|---|---|---|---|
| 278 | | S/O 2-8-0DH | Severn Lamb | 1986 |

This Severn Lamb train is just one of over 40 different attractions set in Paultons' gardens and parkland.

*The Rio Grande Miniature Railway, built by Severn Lamb, takes visitors for a ride past the animal paddocks and through lakeside woods at Paultons Park.*

## RIVERVIEW MINIATURE RAILWAY  *7¹/₄in gauge*

Riverview Garden Centre, Stopham Road, Pulborough, West Sussex RH20 1DS
Telephone: 01798 872981   OS Ref: TQ033183   Operators A. & M. Jones
Line length: 780yd   First opened: 1984

| No | Name | Type | Builder | Built |
|---|---|---|---|---|
| | | 0-6-0BE | Compass House | 1984 |
| 33008 | | 4-4wPH | | |
| | *Hercules* | 0-4-0T | D. Underhill | 1984 |
| | | 2-6-0 | A. Jones | 1998 |

This line, at the back of the garden centre, has already had several layouts. It now features a two-road station, and is to be extended so as to run to a new picnic and adventure playground site. A further extension is under construction.

*No 5 Hercules backs on to the train at Hythe station, Romney Hythe & Dymchurch Railway, on 13 June 1994.* Simon Townsend

## ROMNEY, HYTHE & DYMCHURCH RAILWAY  *15in gauge*

New Romney, Kent TN28 0PL
Telephone: 01797 362353   OS Ref (Hythe): TR153347
Operator: The Romney, Hythe & Dymchurch Light Railway Co Ltd
Line length: 13⅝ miles, balloon   First opened: 1927

| No | Name | Type | Builder | Built |
|----|------|------|---------|-------|
| 1 | *Green Goddess* | 4-6-2 | Davey Paxman | 1925 |
| 2 | *Northern Chief* | 4-6-2 | Davey Paxman | 1925 |
| 3 | *Southern Maid* | 4-6-2 | Davey Paxman | 1926 |
| 4 | *The Bug* | 0-4-0 | Krauss | 1926 |
| 5 | *Hercules* | 4-8-2 | Davey Paxman | 1926 |
| 6 | *Samson* | 4-8-2 | Davey Paxman | 1926 |
| 7 | *Typhoon* | 4-6-2 | Davey Paxman | 1926 |
| 8 | *Hurricane* | 4-6-2 | Davey Paxman | 1926 |
| 9 | *Winston Churchill* | 4-6-2 | Yorkshire Engine | 1931 |
| 10 | *Doctor Syn* | 4-6-2 | Yorkshire Engine | 1931 |
| 11 | *Black Prince* | 4-6-2 | Krupp | 1937 |
| 12 | *John Southland* | 4w-4wDH | TMA Engineering | 1983 |
| 14 | | 4w-4wDH | TMA Engineering | 1989 |
| PW2 | | 2w-2PM | RH&DR | 1962 |
| PW3 | *Redgauntlet* | 4wPM | Alan Keef | 1977 |
| 4 | | 4wDM | Motor Rail | 1938 |

The RH&DR is probably the best known miniature railway in the world. It is a complete railway system in miniature with comprehensive construction and maintenance facilities. There are six stations, eleven steam locomotives, two passenger diesels and three  small i/c powered engines for permanent way work. Passenger coaches (almost seventy in number) include a licenced 'Bar Car' which is the longest vehicle built to run on  15in gauge. The section between Hythe and New Romney is double track.

## ROYAL VICTORIA RAILWAY  *10¹/₄in gauge*

Royal Victoria Country Park, Netley, Southampton SO31 5GA
Telephone (E): 01344 621286   OS Ref: SU464079   Operator: P. Bowers
Line length: 1 mile, circular   First opened: 1990

| No | Name | Type | Builder | Built |
|----|------|------|---------|-------|
| | *Maurice the Major* | 4w-4wDH | P. Bowers | 1996 |
| | *Isambard Kingdom Brunel* | 2-6-0 | D. Curwen | 1977 |

This new line uses part of the trackbed of an earlier 10¹/₄in gauge railway, but is far more ambitious than its predecessor. A further steam locomotive is under construction, and planning permission has been granted for a terminus station, carriage shed/tunnel and a further ¹/₂-mile of track. Definitely a line that deserves success, in this popular public park next to Southampton Water.

## STRAND MINIATURE RAILWAY  *7¹/₄in gauge*

Strand Lido, Gillingham, Kent
OS Ref: TQ785694   Operator: Gillingham Borough Council
Line length: 400yd, circular   First opened: c1951

| No | Name | Type | Builder | Built |
|----|------|------|---------|-------|
| 253003 | *HMS Pembroke* | 4-4wPH | Mardyke | c1980 |
| 112 | | 6w-6wDH | Mardyke | 1987 |

A simple line from Apache station around the Lido, on the seafront at Gillingham.

## SWANLEY NEW BARN RAILWAY  *7¹/₄in gauge*

New Barn Park, Swanley, Kent
OS Ref: TQ515696   Line length: 800yd, balloon   First opened: 1986

| No | Name | Type | Builder | Built |
|----|------|------|---------|-------|
| | | 4w-4BE | Pfeifferbahn | 1986 |
| D9015 | *Tulyar* | 6w-6wDH | Mardyke | 1987 |
| D7612 | *(Steptoe)* | 4w-4wPH | E. Ward | 1988 |
| | | 0-4-0 | P. Beale | 1988 |
| D7076 | | 4w-4wDH | Mardyke | 1989 |
| | | 0-4-0WT | L. Wood | 1990 |
| | *Pierant Taid* | 0-4-0ST | Charles/Meredith | 1988 |
| (47512) | *County of Kent* | 6w-6wDH | Mardyke | 1992 |
| | *Lady Sarah* | 0-4-0T | J. Drury | 1984 |
| | *Owd Rosie* | 2-6-2T | J. Stubbs | 1992 |
| 414 | *Montezuma* | 2-8-0 | J. Stubbs | 1994 |

Trains depart from Lakeside station around an extended loop to New Barn, and return. This line features intricate signalling; its lever frame previously saw service on London Underground.

## WELLINGTON COUNTRY PARK RAILWAY  *7¹/₄in gauge*

Wellington Country Park, Riseley, nr Heckfield, Hampshire RG7 1SP
Telephone: 0118 932 6444   OS Ref: SU730627   Operator: R. Hammond
Line length: 500yd, balloon   First opened: 1980   Park entry fee

| No | Name | Type | Builder | Built |
|----|------|------|---------|-------|
| 425 | *Ivor* | 0-6-0 | J. Liversage | 1949 |
| | *Jingling Geordie* | 8wPM | R. Hammett | |
| | *King Tut* | 2-4-2 | S. Smith | 1934 |

An out-and-back line with a fair sized terminus and shed. Ray Hammond used to build and overhaul locos in the shed here.

## WOKING GRANGE MINIATURE RAILWAY  *6in and 7¹/₄in gauge*

Woking Homes Railcare Centre, Oriental Road, Woking, Surrey
Telephone (E): 01703 440179   OS Ref: TQ014591
Operator: Woking Grange Miniature Railway   Line length: 260yd, end to end
First opened: 1960

| No | Name | Type | Builder | Built |
|----|------|------|---------|-------|
| *6in gauge:* | | | | |
| 870 | *Frederick R. Hutchinson* | 4-6-2 | F. R. Hutchinson | 1925 |
| 486 | | 4-6-0 | F. R. Hutchinson | 1910 |
| | *Canon Allen Edwards* | 4wBE | Barney/Millard | c1979 |
| *7¹/₄in gauge:* | | | | |
| 92203 | *Black Prince* | 2-10-0 | D. Pownall | 1979 |
| 45157 | | 4-6-0 | | |
| | *Wendy* | 0-4-0ST | M. Rickers | 1980 |

A line in the grounds of Railcare Homes, running from Oriental Road to Jeffrey's Road station.

## WOODLAND RAILWAY  *10¹/₄in gauge*

Hotham Park, Bognor Regis, West Sussex
OS Ref: SZ938995   Operator: J. Hudell   Line length: 900yd, circular
First opened: 1969

| No | Name | Type | Builder | Built |
|----|------|------|---------|-------|
| | *John Owen* | 4-4wPM | J. Hudell | 1985 |
| | *Lion* | 0-4-2 | J. Hudell | 1992 |

A circuit through woodland in Hotham Park, with the station next to a small amusement park. This line has recently been taken over and rebuilt by John Hudell, who also ran these locomotives at two earlier locations.

## BARKING RAILWAY  *9¹/₂in gauge*

Barking Park, Longbridge Road, Barking, Greater London
OS Ref: TQ446847   Line length: 350yd, end to end   First opened: 1954

| No | Name | Type | Builder | Built |
|----|------|------|---------|-------|
| | *Little Nan* | 4w-4wPE | Barking Corp | 1961 |

This line runs between Lodge and Lake stations, on virtually a straight alignment. The loco runs round its train at each end.

## BEALE RAILWAY  *10¹/₄in gauge*

Beale Park, Lower Basildon, Pangbourne, Berkshire RG8 9NH
Telephone: 0118 984 5172   OS Ref: SU618782   Operator: J. Treble-Parker
Line length: 1,000yd, dumb-bell   First opened: 1989   Park entry fee

| No | Name | Type | Builder | Built |
|----|------|------|---------|-------|
| | *Sir Humphry Davy* | 4w-4wPM | G&SLE | 1960 |

Between 1989 and 1994 a 7¹/₄in gauge railway operated around this bird park. Now 10¹/₄in gauge tracks have been laid, largely following the earlier line's alignment.

## BLENHEIM PARK RAILWAY  *15in gauge*

Blenheim Palace, Woodstock, Oxfordshire OX20 1PX
Telephone: 01993 811091   OS Ref: SP443162   Operator: Blenheim Estate
Line length: 1,000yd end to end   First opened: 1975   Park entry fee

| No | Name | Type | Builder | Built |
|----|------|------|---------|-------|
| | *Sir Winston Churchill* | S/O 0-6-2DH | Alan Keef | 1992 |
| | *Anna* | 4-6wDM | G&SLE | 1960 |

This line performs a useful transport function, carrying visitors from the Palace entrance down the hill to the garden centre. On peak days the train will be full as soon as the loco has run round, and then it will be off for its next trip.

*0-6-2DH* Sir Winston Churchill *approaches the terminus next to Blenheim Palace on 16 June 1996.* Simon Townsend

## EAST HERTS MINIATURE RAILWAY  *7¹/₄in gauge*

Van Hage Garden Centre, Great Amwell, Hertfordshire
OS Ref: TL367124  Operator: East Herts Miniature Railway Society
Line length: 580yd, complex  First opened: 1978

| No | Name | Type | Builder | Built |
|----|------|------|---------|-------|
| | *H. G. Harrison* | 0-4-0PM | B. Moretti | 1977 |
| | *Hapi* | 2w-2-2wBE | P. Smith | c1987 |
| | *Dolbadarn* | 0-4-0ST | A. Robelou | c1983 |
| | *John A. Patten* | 2-6-2PH | Barnard/Patten | 1991 |
| | *Elf* | 2w-2-2wBE | P. Smith | 1993 |
| | *T. C. B. Miller* | 0-4-2T | A. Robelou | 1991 |
| | *Romulus* | 0-4-0 | C. Farmer | c1985 |
| | *Saint George* | 0-4-0 | A. Cairns/ESSE | 1991 |

This line has two circuits, one inside the other, linked by a diamond crossover. The outer line includes a tunnel, whilst the inner one passes over a bridge.

## FANCOTT LIGHT RAILWAY  *7¹/₄in gauge*

Fancott Arms Public House, Fancott, nr Toddington, Bedfordshire
OS Ref: TL022278  Operator: A. Wallman  Line length: 300yd, balloon
First opened: 1996

| No | Name | Type | Builder | Built |
|----|------|------|---------|-------|
| 1 | | 0-4-0 | Dreadnought | 1994 |

## GREAT WOBURN RAILWAY  *20in gauge*

Woburn Safari Park, Woburn, Bedfordshire MK17 9QN
Telephone: 01525 290407  OS Ref: SP960340  Operator: Woburn Safari Park
Line length: 1,000yd, balloon  First opened: 1994  Park entry fee

| No | Name | Type | Builder | Built |
|----|------|------|---------|-------|
| | *Robin Hood* | S/O 4-6-4DH | Hudswell Clarke | 1932 |
| 4472 | *Flying Scotsman* | S/O 4-6-2DH | Hudswell Clarke | 1933 |

This line runs from a terminus at Bison Halt, through a passing loop, to reach a sharply curved balloon loop, on the farthest side of which is Elephant Junction. The stock previously ran at Morecambe.

## KNEBWORTH PARK MINIATURE RAILWAY  *10¹/₄in gauge*

Knebworth Park, nr Stevenage, Hertfordshire SG3 6PY
Telephone: 01438 812661  OS Ref: TL234215  Operator: S. Madgin
Line length: 800yd, dumb-bell  First opened: 1991

| No | Name | Type | Builder | Built |
|----|------|------|---------|-------|
| | *Uncle Jim* | 4-4wDM | J. Hughes | 1968 |
| | *Meteor IV* | 2-4w-2DM | Shepperton Metal Products | 1969 |
| | *Rhuddlan Castle* | 4w-4wDH | Fenlow | 1972 |
| | *John Glenn* | 4wPM | Cocks/Fairweather | 1994 |
| | *Meteor V* | 2-4w-2PM | Shepperton Metal Products | 1970 |

| No | Name | Type | Builder | Built |
|----|------|------|---------|-------|
| | *Fran* | 2-4w-2PM | B. Chapman | 1998 |
| | *Exmoor Enterprise* | 6-6wPH | Curwen & Newbery | 1965 |

This line runs through the grounds of Knebworth Park, adjacent to the car access to Knebworth House. The station is at the top of a short balloon loop, from where the line wends its way down before crossing to the opposite hillside. Like five of the locomotives, the coaches here also derive from Ian Allan Ltd's foray into miniature railway supplies.

## LITTLE GIANT RAILWAY   *10¹/₄in gauge*

Merton Abbey Mills, Watermill Way, Merton, Greater London SW19
OS Ref: TQ264697   Operator: J. Crosskey   Line length: 120yd, end to end
First opened: 1997

| No | Name | Type | Builder | Built |
|----|------|------|---------|-------|
| | *Lynton* | 2-4-4T | J. Haylock/D. Yates | 1984 |
| | *Donegal* | 4-4wBE | T. Smith | 1975 |

*Lynton* has had a nomadic career, along with its rolling stock and sectional track making up the 'Narrower Gauge Railway'. Now owned by John Crosskey, a permanent line has very recently been established at Merton Abbey Mills.

## LONDON TOY & MODEL MUSEUM   *7¹/₄in gauge*

21/23 Craven Hill, Paddington, London W2 3EN
Telephone: 0171 706 8000   OS Ref: TQ263809   Operator: Toy Museum Ltd
Line length: 75yd, circular   First opened, 1982

| No | Name | Type | Builder | Built |
|----|------|------|---------|-------|
| 1 | *Bear 1* | 0-4-0ST | B. Plant | 1984 |
| | *Winifred* | 0-4-0ST | F. Smith | 1986 |
| | | 4wBE | Maxitrak | 1984 |
| | | S/O 0-4-0BE | Maxitrak | 1988 |

London Toy & Model Museum is the museum of commercially made toys and models. Squeezed into the back garden is this short line; one 'ride' is three times round. Steam trains run at weekends. There are also Gauge 1 and G scale railways.

## PARADISE WILDLIFE PARK WOODLAND RAILWAY   *10¹/₄in gauge*

Paradise Wildlife Park, White Stubbs Lane, Broxbourne, Hertfordshire EN10 7QA
Telephone: 01992 468001   OS Ref: TL338068   Operator: Paradise Wildlife Park
Line length: 440yd, circular   First opened: 1981   Park entry fee

| No | Name | Type | Builder | Built |
|----|------|------|---------|-------|
| | | S/O 2-4w-2DM | Shepperton Metal Products | *c*1971 |

This sit-in steam outline loco hauls its two coaches around a circuit in part of the wildlife park.

*At Paradise Wildlife Park Woodland Railway, the 10¹/₄in gauge 'Meteor' class 2-4w-2DM has been rebuilt with this tall steam outline body.*

Lady of the Lakes *hauling a train on the Ruislip Lido Railway.* Robin Butterell

## RUISLIP LIDO RAILWAY  *12in gauge*

Ruislip Lido, Reservoir Road, Ruislip, Middlesex HA4 7TY
Telephone: 01895 622595   OS Ref: TQ089889
Operator: Ruislip Lido Railway Society Ltd.   Line length: 1¹/₄ miles, balloon
First opened: 1945

| No | Name | Type | Builder | Built |
|----|------|------|---------|-------|
| 3 | *Robert* | 4w-4DH | Severn Lamb | 1973 |
| 5 | *Lady of the Lakes* | 4w-4wDH | Ravenglass & Eskdale Rly | 1985 |
| 7 | *Graham Alexander* | 4w-4wDH | Severn Lamb | 1990 |

This line has improved beyond recognition since beng taken over by volunteers in 1979. Trains now run from the original station at Woody Bay, through the loop at Eleanor's to Haste Hill, then over the new extension to Lakeside, not far from the Lido's main entrance. A steam loco is under construction for the railway. Movements are controlled by radio from the signalbox at Woody Bay. Although run wholly by volunteers, the line is maintained and operated to the highest professional standards.

## SOUTHILL LIGHT RAILWAY  *7¹/₄in gauge*

White Horse Public House, Southill, nr Biggleswade, Bedfordshire
OS Ref: TL148418   Line length: 300yd, circular   First opened: 1984

| No | Name | Type | Builder | Built |
|----|------|------|---------|-------|
|    | *Herbie* | 4w-4PH | Severn Lamb | 1984 |

An ingenious line running from Muchale Junction, with the circuit crossing over itself twice as well as underneath itself and through a tunnel.

## SYON PARK MINIATURE RAILWAY  *10¹/₄in gauge*

Syon Park, London Road  Brentford, Middlesex TW8 8JF
Telephone: 0181 560 0881   OS Ref: TQ173770
Operators: A. Thompson & M. Lugg   Line length: 400yd, end to end
First opened: 1993

| No | Name | Type | Builder | Built |
|------|------------|-------|-------------|------|
| 6220 | *Coronation* | 4-6-2 | E. Dove | 1946 |
| 6100 | *Royal Scot* | 4-6-0 | Carland Eng | 1949 |

A steam hauled out-and-back run from the station adjacent to the gardens' entrance at Syon Park.

*Coronation* is an elegant and practical machine which previously ran for some years at Christchurch.

*Driver Richard Niven demonstrates the controls of 4-6-2* Coronation *to a young visitor to Syon Park.*

38

## VANSTONE WOODLAND RAILWAY  *10¹/₄in gauge*

Vanstone Park and Garden Centre, Hitchin Road, Codicote, nr Stevenage, Hertfordshire
Telephone: 01438 820412   OS Ref: TL215201   Operator: S. Madgin
Line length: 560yd   First opened: 1986

| No | Name | Type | Builder | Built |
|----|------|------|---------|-------|
| | *Sandham Castle* | 2-4w-2DM | Shepperton Metal Products | 1969 |
| | *Thomas* | 0-4-0ST | J. Brown | 1986 |
| | *Meteor VI* | 2-4w-2DM | Shepperton Metal Products | 1970 |

The track here is basically a circuit, but with the station on a siding into which the train is propelled at the end of each run. The wooded section of the line includes some steep gradients. *Thomas* is kept here but only steamed occasionally.

## WATER HALL FARM RAILWAY  *10¹/₄in gauge*

Water Hall Farm and Craft Centre, Whitwell, Stevenage, Hertfordshire
OS Ref: TL187212   Operator: R. Bonfield   Line length: 200yd, circular
First opened: 1993

| No | Name | Type | Builder | Built |
|----|------|------|---------|-------|
| | *The Goyle* | 4w-4PM | Ford | |

## WATFORD MINIATURE RAILWAY  *10¹/₄in gauge*

Cassiobury Park, Watford, Hertfordshire
OS Ref: TQ090972   Operator: J. Price   Line length: 700yd, balloon
First opened: 1959

| No | Name | Type | Builder | Built |
|----|------|------|---------|-------|
| 4179 | *Chiltern Shuttle* | 0-6-0 | R. Morse | 1946 |
| 7 | *Marri* | 2-6-0 | Willis Engineering | 1993 |
| | *Conway Castle* | 4w-4wDH | Fenlow | 1972 |
| | *Meteor II* | 2-4w-2DM | Shepperton Metal Products | 1969 |

*On busy days at the Watford Miniature Railway, 2-6-0 Marri can often be found hauling a 10 coach train. Malcolm Shelmerdine*

This busy line has its station adjacent to the paddling pool/playground area in Cassiobury Park. Passengers ride over a gated crossing and then round upon themselves in an area adjacent to the River Gade, a total journey of 1,020yd. *Marri* is a very powerful machine which was built in Australia, and imported especially for use here; it has an unusual 'Briggs' firebox. At peak times operation here can be very slick indeed; other locos visit occasionally.

## WILLEN MINIATURE RAILWAY  7¹/₄in gauge

Willen Watersports Centre, Milton Keynes, Buckinghamshire
OS Ref: SP877397   Operator: F. Kenny   Line length: 800yd, balloon
First opened: 1989

| No | Name | Type | Builder | Built |
|----|------|------|---------|-------|
| 2 | *Ladybird* | 2-6-4T | F. Kenny | 1992 |

A there-and-back line in a corner of this large public park, popular for its watersports facilities.

*A busy scene at the Willen Miniature Railway in September 1994, with 2-6-4T* Ladybird *about to set off for another trip. Dave Holroyde*

## COALYARD MINIATURE RAILWAY  *7¹/₄in gauge*

Severn Valley Railway, Kidderminster Town Station, Comberton Hill, Kidderminster, Hereford & Worcester DY10 1QX
Telephone: 01562 744667   OS Ref: SO837762
Operator: Coalyard M R Group   Line length: 450yd, end to end
First opened: 1988

| No | Name | Type | Builder | Built |
|---|---|---|---|---|
|  | (*Percy*) | 0-4-0WT | K. Wilson | 1994 |
| D2958 | *Rusty* | 4wPH | R. Dawson | 1992 |
| 5 |  | 4w-2PH | B. & R. Shaw | 1990 |

This line runs from a terminus in front of Kidderminster Railway Museum, out and back parallel to the Severn Valley Railway platforms. All funds raised go towards improving the miniature railway or are donated to restoration projects on the SVR. The railway normally operates on Saturdays from March to December, and to coincide with the SVR's special events.

*The essence of the 7¹/₄in gauge scene, shown here with the 0-4-0WT 'Romulus' on the Coalyard Miniature Railway.*
Richard Shaw

## DRAYTON MANOR PARK MINIATURE RAILWAYS  *10¹/₄in gauge*

Drayton Manor Family Fun Park, Fazeley, nr Tamworth, Staffordshire B79 8HH
Telephone: 01827 287979   OS Ref: SK194016   Operators: The Bryan family
Line lengths: 800yd, circular   First opened: 1951   Park entry fee
600yd, end to end

| No | Name | Type | Builder | Built |
|---|---|---|---|---|
| 278 |  | S/O 2-8-0PH | Severn Lamb | 1971 |
| 7, 278 |  | S/O 2-8-0DH | Severn Lamb | 1983 |

It was Mr G. Bryan, chairman of Drayton Manor, who first ordered the now ubiquitous 'Rio Grande' 2-8-0 from Severn Lamb, along with the distinctive canopied coaches which seat two side by side. They still run this original locomotive, along with a second 'Rio' which operates on a separate track.

*Loco builder Bob Washington drives his 0-6-0PH* Deudraeth Castle *on the Eckington Narrow Gauge Railway.*

## ECKINGTON NARROW GAUGE RAILWAY  *7¹/₄in gauge*

Beacons Nurseries, Tewkesbury Road, Eckington, Pershore, Hereford & Worcester WR10 3DG
Telephone: 01386 750359   OS Ref: SO924411   Operator: R. Washington
Line length: 400yd, end to end   First opened: 1996

| No | Name | Type | Builder | Built |
|---|---|---|---|---|
| | *Tiny Tim* | 0-4-0PH | R. Washington | 1993 |
| | *Deudraeth Castle* | 0-6-0PH | R. & L. Washington | 1995 |
| No 4 | *Triumph* | 4wPM | M. Tebbett | 1984 |

A there-and-back run adjacent to the nursery. *Deudraeth Castle* is a model of *Harlech Castle* on the Ffestiniog Railway; it is unusual on 7¹/₄in gauge in being both a model and enabling the driver to sit inside the cab. This line only opens on Saturdays, from 2pm.

## FINNEY GARDENS RAILWAY  *7¹/₄in gauge*

Finney Gardens, Bucknall Park, Stoke on Trent, Staffordshire
OS Ref: SJ900476   Operator: Stoke on Trent Model Engineers Ltd
Line length: 500yd   First opened: 1996

| No | Name | Type | Builder | Built |
|----|------|------|---------|-------|
| 407 | *Old Rube* | 2-8-0 | Milner Engineering | 1983 |
| | *Lady Be* | 0-4-0ST | D. J. Bussey | 1988 |
| 1 | *Biddy* | 0-4-0T | M. Williams | 1985 |
| 3 | *Jill* | 0-4-0ST | R. Gray | 1993 |
| | | 4w-4wDH | Stoke on Trent MES | 1996 |
| 6 | *Waldenburg* | 0-6-0T | R. Hammond | 1997 |

This new line features a substantial enclosed station and two parallel steel bridges over the River Trent. Ultimately the track will be circular, but pending construction of the second half a turning wye has been built, with a leg of the wye on one of the bridges.

## GWR MUSEUM MINIATURE RAILWAY  *7¹/₄in gauge*

GWR Museum, Old Goods Shed, Coleford, Gloucestershire
OS Ref: SO574107   Operator: M. Rees  Line length: 150yd, circular
First opened: 1988

| No | Name | Type | Builder | Built |
|----|------|------|---------|-------|
| | *Little John* | 4-4wBER | T. Smith | 1979 |
| 2091 | *Victor* | 0-4-0ST | K. Hardy | c1984 |
| | | 4wBE | M. Rees/Maxitrak | c1989 |

A circular line running around this museum, in the old goods shed at Coleford.

*A lull between activities at the Hilcote Valley Railway, with* Kashmir *and 0-4-0ST Hunslet* Lady Madcap *visible.* Dave Holroyde

## HILCOTE VALLEY RAILWAY  *7¹/₄in gauge*

Fletchers Country Garden Centre, Eccleshall, Staffordshire
Telephone (E): 01785 284553   OS Ref: SJ842292   Operator: R Greatrex
Line length: 800yd, circular   First opened: 1993

| No | Name | Type | Builder | Built |
|----|------|------|---------|-------|
| | *Kashmir* | 0-6-0T | M. Marshall/D. Underhill | 1993 |
| | *Lady Madcap* | 0-4-0ST | K. Massey | 1991 |
| | | 6wPH | R. Greatrex | 1998 |
| 6141 | *The North Staffordshire Regiment* | 4-6-0 | R. Greatrex | 1998 |

Roger Greatrex is now a full time builder of miniature railway equipment, and this line is a good showcase for his abilities. The railway runs around the play area, then out behind the garden centre and round a small lake.

## LEASOWES MINIATURE RAILWAY  *7¹/₄in gauge*

Leasowes Park, Mucklow Hill, Halesowen, West Midlands
OS Ref: SO976840   Operator: M. Male
Line length: 400yd, end to end   First opened: 1990

| No | Name | Type | Builder | Built |
|----|------|------|---------|-------|
| 46210 | *Prince Edward* | 2-6-2 | J. & W. Gower | 1936 |
| 45016 | *William Shenstone* | 4-4wPM | M. Male | 1991 |

The line runs along a canal towpath with views overlooking the lake and park, which is grade one listed. The railway operates on Sundays all year round, from 2pm.

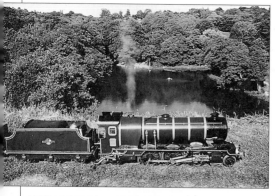

*2-6-2 Prince Edward glints in the sun in front of Breaches Pool, Leasowes Park Miniature Railway.*

## LEISURERAIL STEAM RAILWAY  *7¹/₄in gauge*

Hollybush Garden Centre, Warstone Road, Shareshill,
Wolverhampton WV10 7LX
Telephone: 01922 418050   OS Ref: SJ966064   Operator: Leisurerail Ltd
Line length: 950yd, circular   First opened: 1996

| No | Name | Type | Builder | Built |
|----|------|------|---------|-------|
|    | *Malandra* | 0-4-2 | TMA Engineering | 1987 |
|    | *Kestrel* | 4w-4wPH | E. Smith | 1991 |
|    | *Samuel Whitbread* | 0-4-2 | Roberts/Forshaw | 1986 |

The circuit runs around two small lakes, and features a tunnel and a bridge over a stream.

## MALVERN HILLS NARROW GAUGE RAILWAY   7¹/₄in gauge

Malvern Hills Animal and Bird Garden, Dane Moor, Welland, Hereford & Worcester
Telephone: 01684 310016   OS Ref: SO802410   Operator: C. Cox
Line length: 400yd, circular   First opened: 1986   Zoo entry fee

| No | Name | Type | Builder | Built |
|----|------|------|---------|-------|
| 3039 |    | 4-4wPM | D. Curwen | 1970 |

A simple line running through the paddocks of this small zoo.

## PERRYGROVE RAILWAY   15in gauge

Treasure Train, Perrygrove Farm, Coleford, Gloucestershire GL16 8QB
Telephone: 01594 834991   OS Ref: SO579095   Operator: Treasure Train Ltd
Line length: 1,300yd, end to end   First opened: 1996

| No | Name | Type | Builder | Built |
|----|------|------|---------|-------|
|    | *Spirit of Adventure* | 0-6-0T | Exmoor Steam Railway | 1993 |
| 2  | *Workhorse* | 4wDH | Motor Rail | 1967 |

*The narrow gauge outline of the Perrygrove Railway is clearly evident in this photo of* Spirit of Adventure *and her train on 10 August 1996.* Simon Townsend

Situated just to the south of Coleford, Michael Crofts' railway is based firmly on the minimum gauge principles first promoted by Sir Arthur Heywood a hundred years ago. The line takes the form of a squashed 'S'; trains double back upon themselves at a higher level, before sweeping round and climbing the grade to Oakiron. Children can follow the clues to be rewarded with discoveries of treasure.

## RUDYARD LAKE RAILWAY  *10¹/₄in gauge*

Rudyard Old Station, Rudyard, Leek,  Staffordshire ST13 8PF
Telephone: 01260 272862   OS Ref: SJ956579   Operator: P. Hanton
Line length: 1¹/₄ miles, end to end   First opened: 1978

| No | Name | Type | Builder | Built |
|----|------|------|---------|-------|
| 1 | *Kingsley* | 0-4-0DM | Curwen & Newbery | 1954 |
| 2 | | 4wPM | T. Stanhope | 1969 |
| 5013 | *Ivanhoe* | 4-4-0 | H. Bullock | 1937 |
| 5 | *Rudyard Lady* | 4-4wDM | L. Smith | 1989 |
| 6 | *River Churnet* | 2-4-2T | Exmoor Steam Railway | 1993 |

This line runs along a wooded standard gauge trackbed, from the car park to The Dam, Lakeside, and Hunt House Wood; a very attractive setting for a miniature railway. A steam boat gives rides on the lake nearby.

## SAFARI EXPRESS  *15in gauge*

West Midland Safari & Leisure Park, Spring Grove, Bewdley,
Hereford & Worcester DY12 1LF
Telephone: 01299 402114   OS Ref: SO804756
Operator: W. M. Leisure & Safari Park   Line length: 700yd, end to end
First opened: 1979   Park entry fee

| No | Name | Type | Builder | Built |
|----|------|------|---------|-------|
| 278 | | S/O 2-8-0DH | Severn Lamb | 1979 |

This Severn Lamb train ferries visitors from a station near the park entrance round to the 'leisure area' where many other amusement rides can be found.

## THE NICKELODEON LINE  *12¹/₄in gauge*

Ashorne Hall Nickelodeon, Ashorne Hill, Nr Warwick,
Warwickshire CV33 9QN
Telephone: 01926 651444   OS Ref: SP314587   Operator: G. Whitehead
Line length: 1,000yd, balloon   First opened: 1994

| No | Name | Type | Builder | Built |
|----|------|------|---------|-------|
| | *Ashorne* | 2-4-2T | Exmoor Steam Railway | 1994 |
| | *Bella* | 2-4-2PH | Exmoor S R/P. Camps | 1994 |

*Driver Steve Bell stands next to 2-4-2T* Ashorne *on the 12¹/₄in gauge Nickelodeon Line.*
Robin Butterell

Ashorne Hall houses the Nickelodeon collection of mechanical music, along with a 'Mighty Cinema Organ' upon which there are performances on most opening days at 4pm. In the grounds of the hall the Nickelodeon Line runs from Orange Blossom Halt around and up, through the tunnel, round the loop and back; trains call at New Lodge station on the return journey. Notwithstanding the minimum gauge of this line (made necessary by its curves and grades), its constructors have paid particular attention to detail; notice the ornate coaches, picturesque stations and stock shed.

## WESTON PARK RAILWAY  7¹/₄in gauge

Weston Park, Weston under Lizard, Nr Shifnal, Staffordshire TF11 8LE
Telephone: 01952 850207   OS Ref: SJ808106
Operator: Weston Park Foundation   Line length: 1,200yd, dumb-bell
First opened: 1980

| No | Name | Type | Builder | Built |
|----|------|------|---------|-------|
| 9 | *Michael Charles Lloyd MBE* | 2-8-0 | A. Glaze | 1975 |
| 2 | *Hilton Queen* | 2-6-0 | J. Liversage | 1950 |
| 6 | | 4w-4DE | F. H. Lloyd | 1965 |
| 4 | | 4w-4DH | Reb F. H. Lloyd | 1958 |
| 5 | | 4wBE | Reb F. H. Lloyd | 1960 |

One of the longest and best maintained 7¹/₄in lines, trains run from the bottom station near the house, up the long hill and onto single track, through the passing loop and then to the top balloon loop among some trees. On the return journey, trains call at the adventure playground station before rolling down over a long viaduct to the bottom station again. The railway runs through an outstanding collection of mature trees on the Weston Park Estate. There is a large shed which can house visiting locomotives, some of which may appear during the operating season.

*The opening ceremony of the extension of the Weston Park Miniature Railway on 15 May 1994.* Robin Butterell

## AMERICAN ADVENTURE WORLD RAILROAD   *15in gauge*

American Adventure World, Shipley, nr Ilkeston, Derbyshire DE7 5SX
Telephone: 01773 531521   OS Ref: SK443444
Operator: American Adventure World   Line length: 1 mile, circular
First opened: 1985   Park entry fee

| No | Name | Type | Builder | Built |
|----|------|------|---------|-------|
| No 1 | | S/O 2-6-0DH | Severn Lamb | 1986 |
| | *General George A. Custer* | S/O 2-6-0DH | Severn Lamb | 1988 |

## HALL LEYS MINIATURE RAILWAY   *9¹/₂in gauge*

Hall Leys Park,  Matlock,  Derbyshire
OS Ref: SK300600   Operator: Miniature Railway Co Ltd
Line length: 200yd, end to end   First opened: 1948

| No | Name | Type | Builder | Built |
|----|------|------|---------|-------|
| | *Little David* | 6wDH | Allcock/Coleby Simkins | 1974 |

A simple line running up and down
the side of Hall leys Park.

## MANOR PARK MINIATURE RAILWAY   *7¹/₄in gauge*

Manor Park Road, Glossop, Derbyshire
OS Ref: SE041947   Operator A. Sowden   Line length: 500yd, balloon
First opened: 1970

| No | Name | Type | Builder | Built |
|----|------|------|---------|-------|
| | *Catherine* | 0-4-0ST | J. Horsfield | 1982 |
| 7 | *Jerry* | S/O 4w-2PM | R. Kay | 1983 |
| | *Galahad* | 4w-4PM | Cromar White | 1970 |
| | *Percy* | 0-4-0T | P. Land | 1988 |
| | *Manor* | 4wPH | Pfeifferbahn | 1993 |
| 91012 | *Sandford* | 4-4wPH | A. Bimpson | 1992 |
| 1 | *Matthews Mining* | 0-4-0PM | J. Pinder | 1984 |

The station here has a run round loop, and the balloon loop can be used as a circuit. There are spurs off the balloon loop to the carriage and loco sheds.

## MARKEATON PARK LIGHT RAILWAY   *15in gauge*
Markeaton Park, Derby, Derbyshire
Telephone (E): 01623 552292   OS Ref: SK335372   Operators: J. & J. Bull
Line length: 1,400yd, end to end   First opened: 1989

| No | Name | Type | Builder | Built |
|----|------|------|---------|-------|
| | *Markeaton Lady* | 0-4-2T | Exmoor Steam Railway | 1996 |
| | *Cromwell* | 4wDH | Ruston & Hornsby | 1960 |

*The Markeaton Park Light Railway, with* Markeaton Lady *and her train shown just after the extended railway opened, in October 1996.* Neville Knight

| | | | |
|---|---|---|---|
| D5902 | 4w-4wDM | J. Brown | 1995 |
| No 6 | 4wDM | Lister | 1952 |

This railway has been greatly extended and improved since it was taken over by John and Jane Bull in 1996. Trains now run from the main car park (entrance from the A38 Derby ring road) through the park and over two major bridges to a second terminus adjacent to the play area at Mundy Halt. Most services are worked by *Markeaton Lady* along with three luxurious enclosed coaches also built by Exmoor Steam Railway.

## MELTON MOWBRAY MINIATURE RAILWAY   10¹/₄in gauge

Egerton Park Sportsground, Leicester Road, Melton Mowbray, Leicestershire
OS Ref: SK750190   Operator: Melton Mowbray Town Estate
Line length: 200yd, circular   First opened: 1975

| No | Name | Type | Builder | Built |
|---|---|---|---|---|
| D1417 | | 2w-2PM | G. Wilcox | 1968 |

A simple line running around the bowling green and play area, next to the River Eye.

## PAVILION GARDENS MINIATURE RAILWAY   10¹/₄in gauge

Pavilion Gardens, St Johns Road, Buxton, Derbyshire SK17 6XN
Telephone: 01298 23114   OS Ref: SK055734
Operator: High Peak Borough Council   Line length: 300yd, circular
First opened: 1972

| No | Name | Type | Builder | Built |
|---|---|---|---|---|
| | *Borough of Buxton* | 2-4w-2DM | Shepperton Metal Products | 1968 |
| | | S/O 4wDH | R. Prime | 1989 |

These 2-6-0s built by Severn Lamb have a more anglicised appearance than the 'Rio Grande' 2-8-0s. This one runs at Queens Park, Chesterfield.

## QUEENS PARK MINIATURE RAILWAY  10¹/₄in gauge

Queens Park, Boythorpe Road, Chesterfield, Derbyshire
Telephone: 01246 345559   OS Ref: SK378709
Operator: Chesterfield Borough Council
Line length: 550yd, circular   First opened: 1976

| No | Name | Type | Builder | Built |
|----|------|------|---------|-------|
|    | (Lady of the Lakes) | S/O 2-6-0DH | Severn Lamb | 1988 |

A train of Severn Lamb stock running around the lake in this public park.

## TWYCROSS ZOO MINIATURE RAILWAY  10¹/₄in gauge

Twycross Zoo, Twycross, nr Atherstone, Leicestershire CV9 3PX
Telephone: 01827 880250   OS Ref: SK320061   Operator: Twycross Zoo
Line length: 600yd, circular   First opened: 1969   Zoo entry fee

| No | Name | Type | Builder | Built |
|----|------|------|---------|-------|
| 7, 278 |  | S/O 2-8-0PH | Severn Lamb | 1983 |

The line here includes a spiral section over which trains descend just after leaving the station. The locomotive was one of a number built carrying numbers 7 on the chimney and 278 on the cab side.

## WHITEPOST WONDERLAND RAILWAY  7¹/₄in gauge

Wonderland Pleasure Park, White Post Corner, Farnsfield, Nottinghamshire NG22 8HX
Telephone: 01623 882773   OS Ref: SK627572   Operator: D. Pepper
Line length: 350yd, balloon   First opened: 1996   Park entry fee

| No | Name | Type | Builder | Built |
|----|------|------|---------|-------|
|    |      | 2-6wDH | Tucktonia | 1986 |

The locomotive here is built around a Mountfield lawn mower. The system's unique feature is that whilst the loco is diesel powered, they operate a synchronised sound track!

## AUDLEY END MINIATURE RAILWAY   *10¹/₄in gauge*

Audley End House, Saffron Walden, Essex
Telephone: 01799 541354   OS Ref: TL523378   Operator: Lord Braybrooke
Line length: 1 mile, dumb-bell   First opened: 1964

| No | Name | Type | Builder | Built |
|---|---|---|---|---|
| 3548 | *Lord Braybrooke* | 2-6-2 | D. Curwen | 1948 |
| D1011 | *Western Thunderer* | 6-6wPM | Curwen & Newbery | 1964 |
| 4433 | | 4-4-2 | Curwen & Newbery | 1965 |
| 489 | *Sara Lucy* | 2-8-2 | D. Curwen | 1977 |
| 682 | *Doris* | 0-6-0PM | D. Curwen | 1982 |
| 691 | *Henrietta Jane* | 0-4-0+0-4-0PH | A. Crowhurst | 1991 |
| 24 | *Linda* | 2-6-2 | D. Curwen | 1991 |
| 1680 | *Loyalty* | 4-4-0 | D. Curwen | 1994 |
| | | 2-4-2 | D. Curwen | 1997 |

A racetrack of a line with an impressive array of locomotives on shed, from a Great Northern Atlantic to an enormous Denver & Rio Grande 2-8-2. Audley End station has its own car park not far from the entrance drive to the house. After passing the shed area, trains bowl along a long straight, then cross the River Fulfen and River Cam. They then enter a very long and curvaceous balloon loop through the woods, passing Forest Deep Halt, and through a long tunnel. The loop points are centre sprung, so alternate trains take this section in opposite directions before returning from whence they came. Watch out for the teddies that live in the woods.

*Differences in scale are apparent between British standard gauge and American 3ft gauge prototypes, both models running on the 10¹/₄in gauge Audley End Miniature Railway, on 12 May 1990. Simon Townsend*

*4-6-2 Britannia hauls a train on the Barleylands Miniature Steam Railway.* W. B. Connoll

## BARLEYLANDS MINIATURE STEAM RAILWAY   *7¹/₄in gauge*

Barleylands Visitor Centre, Barleylands Road, Billericay, Essex CM11 2UD
Telephone: 01268 532253   OS Ref: TQ695920   Operator: H. R. Philpot and
Son (Barleylands) Ltd   Line length: 800yd, end to end   First opened: 1989

| No | Name | Type | Builder | Built |
|---|---|---|---|---|
| | *Maid of Benfleet* | 4-4-2T | J. Clarke | 1970 |
| | *Vulcan* | 2-6-0 | J. Clarke | 1972 |
| 92250 | *Black Prince* | 2-10-0 | J. Clarke | 1981 |
| 70000 | *Britannia* | 4-6-2 | J. Clarke | 1981 |
| | *Gowrie* | 0-6-4T | H Dyson | 1990 |

From the shed area behind the museum, this line drops down in a C shape to a run round loop at Littlewood Junction. From there a further line runs, more or less straight, to Boot Fair station. Because of its layout, the railway is usually operated in two halves. Most of the equipment here came from a notable private railway at Benfleet, alas now closed.

## BASILDON MINIATURE RAILWAY   *10¹/₄in gauge*

Wat Tyler Country Park, Pitsea, Essex
OS Ref: TQ738865   Operator: D. Bundock
Line length: 1,200yd, balloon   First opened: 1988

| No | Name | Type | Builder | Built |
|---|---|---|---|---|
| | *Western Courier* | 6-6wPH | Severn Lamb | 1969 |

A line running through this extensive country park, from the boat museum to the marina.

## BELTON HOUSE MINIATURE RAILWAY   *7¹/₄in gauge*

Belton House, Belton, nr Grantham, Lincolnshire NG32 2LS
Telephone: 01476 566116   OS Ref: SK927394   Operator: The National Trust
Line length: 500yd, end to end   First opened: 1979   Grounds entry fee

| No | Name | Type | Builder | Built |
|---|---|---|---|---|
| E1 | | 6w-6wPH | Mardyke | 1979 |
| | | 4w-4PH | G. Johnson | 1979 |

A simple line running out-and-back through woodlands on the estate of | Belton House.

## BRESSINGHAM STEAM MUSEUM AND GARDENS ▬▬▬▬▬
*15in and 10¹/₄in gauge*

Diss, Norfolk IP22 2AB
Telephone: 01379 687386   OS Ref: TM080805   Operator: Bressingham Steam Preservation Co. Ltd
Waveney Valley Railway; 15in gauge   1¹/₄ miles, circular   First opened: 1973
Garden Railway; 10¹/₄in gauge   700yd, balloon   First opened: 1995

| No | Name | Type | Builder | Built |
|----|------|------|---------|-------|
| *15in gauge* | | | | |
| 1662 | *Rosenkavalier* | 4-6-2 | Krupp | 1937 |
| 1663 | *Mannertreu* | 4-6-2 | Krupp | 1937 |
| | *Ivor* | 4wDH | Frenze Eng | 1979 |
| *10¹/₄in gauge* | | | | |
| 1 | *Alan Bloom* | 0-4-0ST | P. Gray | 1995 |

These miniature lines form two of the attractions at Bressingham Steam Museum. Trains on the Waveney Valley Railway are timed to coincide with those on the 2ft gauge Nursery Line, which crosses over it, so that passengers can see the other train at work. The Garden Railway is an enlarged version of a 9¹/₂in gauge line which dated back to Bressingham's first public opening. Steam days are Sundays, Thursdays and peak Wednesdays. A 15in gauge 4-6-2 *Flying Scotsman* and a 12in gauge 4-4-0T are on display in the museum here.

## BURE VALLEY RAILWAY   *15in gauge* ▬▬▬▬▬

Aylsham, Norfolk NR11 6BW
Telephone: 01263 733858   OS Ref: TG196264
Operator: Bure Valley Railway (1991) Ltd
Line length: 8¹/₂ miles, end to end   First opened: 1990

| No | Name | Type | Builder | Built |
|----|------|------|---------|-------|
| 3 | *Buxton Mill* | 4w-4wDH | J. Edwards | 1989 |
| 1 | *Wroxham Broad* | 2-6-4T | G&SLE | 1964 |
| 6 | *Blickling Hall* | 2-6-2 | Winson Eng | 1994 |
| 7 | *Spitfire* | 2-6-2 | Winson Eng | 1994 |
| 4 | *The Apprentice* | 4wDH | Hunslet | 1954 |
| 7 | | S/O 4wDM | Lister Blackstone | 1960 |
| 8 | | 2-6-2T | BVR/Winson | 1998 |

Trains run from Aylsham through Brampton, Buxton and Coltishall to Wroxham; most of the formation is on a standard gauge trackbed. The 'ZB' class 2-6-2s are among the largest and most powerful 15in gauge locomotives ever built. Special events include 'Friends of Thomas' and Santa trains; the railway also offers driving courses.

2-6-2 No 6 and train stand in Wroxham station, with its well designed building, on the Bure Valley Railway.
Dave Holroyde

2-4-2 Siân prepares to haul a train on the Cleethorpes Coast Light Railway.
Robin Butterell

## CLEETHORPES COAST LIGHT RAILWAY  15in gauge

Lakeside Station, Kings Road, Cleethorpes,  Lincolnshire DN35 0AG
Telephone: 01472 604657   OS Ref: TA315078
Operator: Cleethorpes Coast Light Railway Ltd   Line length: 1,400yd, end to end
First opened: 1971

| No | Name | Type | Builder | Built |
|----|------|------|---------|-------|
| | | S/O 2-8-2DH | Severn Lamb | 1972 |
| | *John* | 4-4wDH | Minirail | 1954 |
| | | 4wDM | Lister | 1944 |
| 4 | *Siân* | 2-4-2 | G&SLE | 1963 |
| 7204 | *Katie* | 2-4-2 | G&SLE | 1956 |

| No | Name | Type | Builder | Built |
|----|------|------|---------|-------|
|    |      | 4wDM | Eclipse Peat | c1956 |
| 24 |      | 2-6-2 | Fairbourne | 1990 |

This is the latest of six different miniature railways to have operated in Cleethorpes over the years, having recently been regauged from 14¼in gauge. Trains run from Lakeside Station up the hill past the shed area, then alongside the sea wall to Kingsway. For many years two Severn Lamb 'Rio's were the sole motive power, but the railway now has a good volunteer support group and trains are regularly steam hauled.

## FELIXSTOWE MINIATURE RAILWAY   7¼in gauge

Sea Road, Felixstowe, Suffolk
OS Ref: TM298339   Operator: Ocean Amusements
Line length: 150yd, circular   First opened: 1960

| No | Name | Type | Builder | Built |
|----|------|------|---------|-------|
|    |      | 4w-4PM | Cromar White | 1971 |
| 350024 |  | 4-4wPH | Mardyke | c1983 |

A small circle of track among the attractions on the promenade at Felixstowe.

## FERRY MEADOWS MINIATURE RAILWAY   10¼in gauge

Nene Park, Oundle Road, Peterborough  Cambridgeshire
Telephone: 01205 364352   OS Ref: TL148975   Operator: Cubedart Ltd
Line length: 700yd, end to end   First opened: 1979

| No | Name | Type | Builder | Built |
|----|------|------|---------|-------|
| 1950 | *Henry* | 4-6-2 | E. Dove | 1950 |
|      | *Ivor* | 0-4-0ST | Jones/Mills | 1993 |
|      | *Maid of Tynne* | 4w-4wDH | A. Mills | 1993 |

A popular line located in a large public park, a short walk from Ferry Meadows station on the Nene Valley Railway. The track descends from Ham Lane to Gunwade Lane; the loco is turned and runs round its train at each end.

## FRITTON LAKE MINIATURE RAILWAY   10¼in gauge

Fritton Lake Countryworld, Fritton, nr Great Yarmouth  Norfolk NR31 9HA
Telephone: 01493 488208   OS Ref: TM477001   Operator: G. Fairweather
Line length: 400yd, balloon   First opened: 1996   Park entry fee

| No | Name | Type | Builder | Built |
|----|------|------|---------|-------|
|    | (*Derek*) | 4wDM | Shepperton Metal Products | 1968 |
|    | *Nevada* | 4-4wPH | A. Bimpson | 1996 |

Fritton Lake is a picturesque country park with numerous facilities for the whole family. The railway runs through woodland and offers views across the two-mile-long lake.

## MALDON MINIATURE RAILWAY  *10¹/₄in gauge*

Promenade Park, Maldon, Essex
OS Ref: TL861065   Line length: 235yd, end to end   First opened: 1948

| No | Name | Type | Builder | Built |
|----|------|------|---------|-------|
|    |      | 4wRE | M Harvey | 1988 |

A simple up and down ride alongside the amusement park, unique in being electrically powered through a raised third rail. There used to be a Carland 'Royal Scot' here, but when its condition deteriorated the resourceful fairground operator made the present machine using parts of its tender.

## PETTITTS ANIMAL ADVENTURE PARK  *10¹/₄in gauge*

Camphill, Reedham, Norfolk NR13 3UA
Telephone: 01493 700094   OS Ref: TG425025   Operator: Pettitts
Line length: 400yd, circular   First opened: 1989   Park entry fee

| No | Name | Type | Builder | Built |
|----|------|------|---------|-------|
|    |      | 4-4wDH | T. Smith | 1973 |
|    |      | S/O 4w-4wDH | Pettitts | 1990 |
|    |      | S/O 6w-6wDH | W. Shearing | 1992 |

Originally 7¹/₄in gauge, the line forms one of the attractions in this animal park. Trains run clockwise from Pettitts Junction.

## PLEASUREWOOD HILLS MINIATURE RAILWAY  *7¹/₄in gauge*

Pleasurewood Hills Family Theme Park, Corton, nr Lowestoft,
Suffolk NR32 5DZ
Telephone: 01502 586000   OS Ref: TM543966   Operator: Pleasureworld Ltd
Line length: 1,300yd, circular   First opened: 1982   Park entry fee

| No | Name | Type | Builder | Built |
|-----|------|------|---------|-------|
| 688 |      | 6w-6wDH | J. Edwards | 1981 |
| 723 | *B. M. Brunning* | 6w-6wDH | Edwards/Hudson | 1984 |

This line runs from Pleasureworld Hills station through the park area, then through a tunnel and into woodland. There is also a 2ft gauge circuit which crosses the 7¹/₄in gauge, once over a bridge and again on the level. It is unusual to find 7¹/₄in gauge working in such a commercial environment.

## QUEENS PARK MINIATURE RAILWAY  *7¹/₄in gauge*

Queens Park  Mablethorpe, Lincolnshire
OS Ref: TF510847   Operator: Mr Farrow   Line length: 200yd, circular
First opened: 1968

| No | Name | Type | Builder | Built |
|----|------|------|---------|-------|
|    | *The Joy Belle* | 4w-4PM | G. Mawby | 1972 |
| 11 |      | S/O 4-4wPM | G. Mawby | 1976 |

Before the World War 2 Louis Shaw and Percy Harding Kiff operated some notable public 7¹/₄in gauge railways in Mablethorpe. Alas all one can see today is this simple circle of track in a public park behind the sea wall, running through the tunnel/shed as it goes.

## SHERWOOD RAIL   *7¹/₄in gauge*

East Anglian Railway Museum, Chappel Station, nr Colchester, Essex CO6 2DS
Telephone: 01206 242524   OS Ref: TL898289
Operator: East Anglian Railway Museum   Line length: 150yd, end to end
First opened: 1991

| No | Name | Type | Builder | Built |
|----|------|------|---------|-------|
| | *Maid Marion* | 0-4-0T | | |
| | | 4wPM | | 1995 |

A short line forming an attraction additional to the standard gauge exhibits at the East Anglian Railway Museum.

## SOMERLEYTON MINIATURE RAILWAY   *7¹/₄in gauge*

Somerleyton Hall & Gardens, Somerleyton, Lowestoft, Suffolk NR32 5QQ
Telephone: 01502 730224   OS Ref: TM491978   Operator: B. Breeze
Line length: 400yd, circular   First opened: 1972   Gardens entry fee

| No | Name | Type | Builder | Built |
|----|------|------|---------|-------|
| 8102 | *Basil Breeze* | 2-4-2 | King/Breeze | 1987 |
| D8000 | | 4w-4PM | B. Breeze | 1981 |
| D7026 | *Somerleyton* | 4w-4PM | Cromar White | 1971 |

A circular line in the grounds of Somerleyton Hall, which has now celebrated 25 years of operation. Open Thursdays and Sundays, and peak Tuesdays and Wednesdays; the railway runs from 3pm.

*A good load on the 'sit astride' coaches of the Somerleyton Miniature Railway, about to depart with 2-4-2* Basil Breeze.

## WELLS AND WALSINGHAM LIGHT RAILWAY  *10¹/₄in gauge*

Wells-next-the-Sea, Norfolk NR23 1QB
Telephone: 01328 710631  OS Ref: TF925430
Operator: Hannay Hill Railway Ltd
Line length: 4 miles, end to end  First opened: 1982

| No | Name | Type | Builder | Built |
|----|------|------|---------|-------|
| | *Norfolk Hero* | 2-6-0+0-6-2 | N. Simkins | 1986 |
| | *Weasel* | 6wDH | Alan Keef | 1985 |

This is the longest 10¹/₄in gauge railway in the world, and was also the first 10¹/₄in gauge railway to obtain a Light Railway Order. Trains run from the station above Wells-next-the-Sea to Walsingham, along a standard gauge trackbed. *Norfolk Hero* takes the great majority of services, which run daily from Good Friday to the end of September. The railway has an active volunteer support group.

*Neil Simkins' masterpiece 2-6-0+0-6-2 Garratt* Norfolk Hero *on the Wells & Walsingham Light Railway, which runs along the trackbed of an abandoned British Rail line.*

## WELLS HARBOUR RAILWAY  *10¹/₄in gauge*

Beach Road, Wells next the Sea, Norfolk
OS Ref: TF915439  Operator: M. Want  Line length: 1,200yd
First opened: 1976

| No | Name | Type | Builder | Built |
|----|------|------|---------|-------|
| | *Edmund Hannay* | 0-4-2WT | D. King | 1971 |
| | (*Weasel*) | 4wPM | D. King | 1980 |

This line was the precursor to the Wells & Walsingham Light Railway. It runs from Harbour station at Wells, alongside the Beach Road to Pinewoods, forming a useful transport service to and from a caravan site. The little locos must by now have notched up a remarkable mileage.

## BLACKPOOL ZOO MINIATURE RAILWAY *15in gauge*

Blackpool Zoo Park, East Park Drive, Blackpool, Lancashire FY3 8PP
Telephone: 01253 765027   OS Ref: SD335362
Operator: Blackpool Miniature Rly Co Ltd   Line length: 800yd, end to end
First opened: 1972   Zoo entry fee

| No | Name | Type | Builder | Built |
|----|------|------|---------|-------|
| 279 | | S/O 2-8-0DH | Severn Lamb | 1972 |

A line running within the grounds of the zoo. Trains every 15 minutes from 10am, March to October; tickets are sold for either single or return journeys.

## BROOKSIDE MINIATURE RAILWAY *7¼in gauge*

Brookside Garden Centre, Macclesfield Road, Poynton, Cheshire
Telephone: 01625 872919   OS Ref: SJ927852
Operator: Brookside Garden Centre Ltd   Line length: 450yd, balloon
First opened: 1990

| No | Name | Type | Builder | Built |
|----|------|------|---------|-------|
| 2 | *Anne* | 4wPH | McFarlane/Pfeifferbahn | 1981 |
| 9 | *Siân* | 0-4-0ST | N. Pendlebury | 1989 |
| D7031 | *Temeraire* | 4-4wPH | Mardyke | 1989 |
| | *Princess* | 0-4-2T | Edgerton/Horsfield | 1989 |
| 3 | *Lady Pauline* | 0-4-2T | A. Kay | 1982 |
| 2 | *David* | 4-4wPH | N. Pendlebury | 1991 |
| 6100 | *Royal Scot* | 4-6-0 | English Electric | 1952 |
| 2 | *Marcus* | 0-4-0ST | A. Kay | 1978 |

*The atmosphere of the Brookside Miniature Railway is enhanced by the large display of railwayana.* Lady Pauline *has a full head of steam, awaiting the next departure.* Robin Butterell

| No | Name | Type | Builder | Built |
|----|------|------|---------|-------|
| 47632 | *Brookside* | 6-6wPH | B. Lomas | 1995 |
| 5 | | 4w-2BH | J. Horsfield | 1996 |
| | | 4-6-0 | N. Wooler/A Kay | 1996 |
| 7 | | S/O 4wBE | Parkside | 1996 |
| | *Thor* | 6-6wPH | B. Lomas | 1998 |

This line runs through a busy garden centre, the scenic route including two river bridges and a 65ft tunnel. At the station is a replica GWR waiting room, inside which an extensive collection of railwayana is displayed. The steam outline 4wBE locomotive runs on its own track; put a coin in the slot and drive your own train.

## CROXTETH PARK MINIATURE RAILWAY   7¹/₄in gauge

Croxteth Hall & Country Park, Croxteth, Merseyside L12 0HB
Telephone: 0151 228 5311   OS Ref: SJ406944
Operator: Forest Model Engineering   Line length: 350yd, circular
First opened: 1981

| No | Name | Type | Builder | Built |
|----|------|------|---------|-------|
| | *Estelle* | 0-4-0T | TMA Engineering | 1981 |
| | *Mardyke Osprey* | 4-4wPH | Mardyke | 1983 |
| | *Mardyke Merlin* | 6w-6PH | Mardyke | 1982 |

The line runs around a small reserved section of this large country park.

## FRONTIERLAND RAILROAD   16in gauge

Frontierland Western Theme Park, The Promenade, Morecambe, Lancashire LA4 4DG
Telephone: 01524 410024   OS Ref: SD428641
Operator: Blackpool Pleasure Beach   Line length: 400yd, circular
First opened: 1987

| No | Name | Type | Builder | Built |
|----|------|------|---------|-------|
| 1865 | | S/O 4w-4-4wPH | Alan Herschell | c1959 |

This line runs among the rides at Frontierland. Alan Herschell are a USA firm, and it would seem that once this unusual train had been imported, the line had to be constructed to suit its gauge.

## GROSVENOR PARK MINIATURE RAILWAY   7¹/₄in gauge

Grosvenor Park, Chester
Telephone (E): 01244 679552   OS Ref: SJ412663
Operators: T. Schofield and R. Butterell   Line length: 340yd, circular
First opened: 1996

| No | Name | Type | Builder | Built |
|----|------|------|---------|-------|
| | *William Gordon* | 6wPH | R. Greatrex | 1994 |
| | *Tinker* | 0-4-2T | M. Carroll/A. Robelou | 1994 |

*Driver Malcolm Carroll eases his 0-4-2T* Tinker *off the viaduct at the Grosvenor Park Miniature Railway in Chester, on 5 April 1997.* Simon Townsend

Built as an adjunct to the Eaton Railway Centenary Exhibition, the line runs round a small lake and features an impressive bridge constructed in 1997.

## GULLIVERS WORLD RAILWAY  *15in gauge*

Gullivers World, Shackleton Close, Old Hall, Warrington, Cheshire WA5 5YZ
Telephone: 01925 444888   OS Ref: SJ589902   Operator: D. Phillips
Line length: 500yd, circular   First opened: 1989

| No | Name | Type | Builder | Built |
|----|------|------|---------|-------|
|  |  | S/O 6+6wDE | Meridian Motioneering | 1989 |

## HAIGH RAILWAY  *15in gauge*

Haigh Country Park, Haigh, Wigan, Greater Manchester
Telephone: 01942 832895   OS Ref: SD599087
Operator: Wigan Metripolitan Borough Council
Line length: 1 mile, circular   First opened: 1986

| No | Name | Type | Builder | Built |
|----|------|------|---------|-------|
| 15 | *W. Brogan MBE* | 0-6-0DM | G&SLE | 1961 |
|  |  | S/O 0-6-2DH | Alan Keef | 1992 |

This line runs through woodland in the country park surrounding Haigh Hall, with stations at Haigh South and Haigh North. Its original stock came from Fairbourne when that railway changed its gauge. Later it also purchased a steam outline locomotive and coaches from Alan Keef Ltd.

## HALTON MINIATURE RAILWAY   *7¹/₄in gauge*

Town Park, Palace Fields, Runcorn, Cheshire
OS Ref: SJ547815   Operator: Halton Miniature Railway Society
Line length: 1 mile   First opened: 1980

| No | Name | Type | Builder | Built |
|----|------|------|---------|-------|
| | *Norton Priory School* | 4w-4PH | Norton Priory School | 1980 |
| | *Geraldine* | 0-4-0PH | ICI Widnes | 1984 |
| 3 | *Buffalo Bill* | S/O 2-8-0PH | A. Bimpson | 1984 |
| 7 | | S/O 0-4-0PH | L. Hough | 1986 |

Trains depart from Mousetrap station, near the park entrance, and shortly bear left onto a very long balloon loop. Halfway along this loop is a chord for trains only taking a 'short' journey. There are several passing loops on the way round, for works trains or where locos may pause if need be. Quite an extensive line; special days are regularly held, during which visiting locomotives often operate.

## HAPPY MOUNT EXPRESS   *10¹/₄in gauge*

Happy Mount Park, Bare, Morecambe, Lancashire
OS Ref: SD456653   Operator: Mrs P. Woodhouse   Line length: 200yd, circular
First opened: c1956

| No | Name | Type | Builder | Built |
|----|------|------|---------|-------|
| | | S/O 4-6-0PH | Sharpe/Martell | 1994 |
| | | 4-4wPH | E. Sharpe | 1982 |

A simple but long established line in the grounds of Happy Mount Park.

*The designer of this 4-6-0PH has shown considerable ingenuity in the design of the 'steam outline' body, on the 10¹/₄in gauge Happy Mount Express, at Morecambe in June 1994.* Dave Holroyde

## KNOWSLEY SAFARI PARK RAILWAY   *15in gauge*

Knowsley Safari Park, Knowsley Hall, Prescot, Merseyside L34 4AN
Telephone: 0151 430 9009   OS Ref: SJ460936   Operator: The Earl of Derby
Line length: 750yd, dumb-bell   First opened: 1971

| No | Name | Type | Builder | Built |
|----|------|------|---------|-------|
| | | S/O 2-6-0DH | Severn Lamb | 1991 |

This line forms one of the amusement attractions adjacent to the entrance to the Safari Park.

*No 4468* Duke of Edinburgh *outside the shed at the Lakeside Miniature Railway, Southport.*
Austin Moss

## LAKESIDE MINIATURE RAILWAY  *15in gauge*

Marine Lake, Southport, Merseyside
OS Ref: SD331174   Operators: Spencer & Gittins
Line length: 700 yds, end to end   First opened: 1911

| No | Name | Type | Builder | Built |
|----|------|------|---------|-------|
| | *Red Dragon* | 4-4-2 | Moss/Walker | 1991 |
| 4468 | *Duke of Edinburgh* | S/O 4-6-2DE | H. Barlow | 1948 |
| 2510 | *Prince Charles* | S/O 4-6-2DE | H. Barlow | 1954 |
| | *Golden Jubilee 1911-1961* | S/O 4-6-0DE | H. Barlow | 1963 |
| | *Princess Anne* | 6-6wDM | Severn Lamb | 1971 |

One of the two oldest lines in the UK, the Lakeside Miniature Railway can claim a continuous record of service since it was opened originally by Mr Llewellyn, a local postman and shop owner. Trains run from Pleasureland station parallel to the Marine Lake, then curve round underneath the pier to reach Happiland. Both termini have two platforms with their own run round loops, so it is possible to operate all three rakes of stock (two loading, one on the move). The steam loco works on some Saturdays. With its brightly painted stations and stock, this line combines the best of fairground and railway traditions.

## LOWTHER MINIATURE RAILWAY  *7¹/₄in gauge*

Lowther Park, Hackthorpe, Penrith, Cumbria CA10 2HG
Telephone: 01931 712523   OS Ref: NY532225   Operator: Lowther Park
Line length: 900yd, dumb-bell   First opened: 1982   Park entry fee

| No | Name | Type | Builder | Built |
|----|------|------|---------|-------|
| | *Rio Grande* | 4w-4PH | A. Bimpson | 1982 |
| 812 | | 6w-6wPH | D. Smallwood | 1991 |

One of many attractions in the leisure park, this line had its own steam loco at one time. The layout is unusual in that the far balloon loop had to be squeezed into a confined space, so it makes a diamond crossing over itself just after the loop points.

## MORECAMBE BAY MINIATURE RAILWAY *10¹/₄in gauge*

West End Gardens, Morecambe, Lancashire
OS Ref: SD423636   Operator: L. Wynn   Line length: 200yd, circular
First opened: 1997

| No | Name | Type | Builder | Built |
|----|------|------|---------|-------|
| 4 | *Stella Nova* | 6w-6wPM | R. Yates | 1979 |
| 5 | | 0-6-0PM | R. Yates | 1985 |

The stock here formerly ran on the Netherhall Woodland Railway at Maryport in Cumbria.

*4-6-2 Mary Louise negotiates a tight curve on the Pleasure Beach Express at Blackpool.*
Robin Butterell

## PLEASURE BEACH EXPRESS *21in gauge*

Pleasure Beach, South Shore, Blackpool, Lancashire FY4 1EZ
Telephone: 01253 341033   OS Ref: SD306333
Operator: Blackpool Pleasure Beach   Line length: 1,000yd, circular
First opened: 1934

| No | Name | Type | Builder | Built |
|------|------|------|---------|-------|
| 4472 | *Mary Louise* | S/O 4-6-2DH | Hudswell Clarke | 1933 |
| 4473 | *Carol Jean* | S/O 4-6-4DH | Hudswell Clarke | 1933 |
| 6200 | *The Princess Royal* | S/O 4-6-2DH | Hudswell Clarke | 1935 |

Ever-popular among the rides at the Pleasure Beach is the miniature railway, which wends its way past a lake and among the foundations for numerous other rides.

## PORT HAVERIGG HOLIDAY VILLAGE RAILWAY   *7¹⁄₄in gauge*

Port Haverigg Holiday Village, Hodbarrow, nr Millom, Cumbria
OS Ref: SD171788   Operator: R & S Attwood   Line length: 400yd, circular
First opened: 1997

| No | Name | Type | Builder | Built |
|----|------|------|---------|-------|
|    |      | 0-4-2T | CSM Engineering | 1997 |
|    |      | 4wPM | V. Crossman | |

## RAVENGLASS AND ESKDALE RAILWAY   *15in gauge*

Ravenglass, Cumbria CA18 1SW
Telephone: 01229 717171   OS Ref: SD086967
Operator: Ravenglass & Eskdale Railway Co Ltd   Line length: 7 miles, end to end
First opened: 1876

| No | Name | Type | Builder | Built |
|----|------|------|---------|-------|
| 7 | *River Irt* | 0-8-2 | A. Heywood | 1894 |
| 6 | *River Esk* | 2-8-2 | Davey Paxman | 1923 |
| ICL No1 | | 4-4wPM | Ravenglass | 1925 |
| | *Quarryman* | 4wPM | Muir Hill | 1926 |
| | *Perkins* | 4w-4DM | Muir Hill | 1929 |
| 9 | *River Mite* | 2-8-2 | H. Clarkson | 1966 |
| | *Shelagh of Eskdale* | 4-6-4DH | Severn Lamb | 1969 |
| 10 | *Northern Rock* | 2-6-2 | R&ER Co | 1976 |
| | *Synolda* | 4-4-2 | Bassett Lowke | 1912 |
| | *Silver Jubilee* | 4 car DMR | R&ER Co | 1976 |
| 1 | *Scooter* | 2-2wPMR | R&ER Co | 1970 |
| ICL8 | *Lady Wakefield* | 4w-4wDH | R&ER Co | 1980 |
| 11 | *Bonnie Dundee* | 0-4-2 | Kerr Stuart | 1901 |
| (U2) | | 4wBE | Greenwood & Batley | 1957 |
| ICL9 | *Cyril* | 4wDM | Lister | 1932 |

*Recently rebuilt 0-4-2* Bonnie Dundee, *with new tender, being turned at Ravenglass.*
Robin Butterell

| No | Name | Type | Builder | Built |
|----|------|------|---------|-------|
| | *The Flower of the Forest* | 2w-2VBT | R&ER Co | 1985 |
| | *Blacolvesley* | S/O 4-4-4PM | Bassett Lowke | 1909 |

The Ravenglass & Eskdale Railway is justifiably marketed as ₮The most beautiful train journey in England'. The line was originally 3ft gauge, but reopened to 15in gauge in 1915. It was nearly scrapped in 1960, but was saved at the last moment by a group of enthusiasts and since then has been improved out of all recognition by dedicated permanent staff and volunteers. The railway's workshops have extensive facilities and two locomotives have been built here for a railway in Japan. Douglas Ferreira, the manager for many years, was recently awarded the OBE for his outstanding contribution. 0-4-0T *Katie* of 1896 is under restoration here.

## SAFARI RAILWAY   *7¹/₄in gauge*

South Lakes Wild Animal Park, Dalton in Furness, Cumbria
Telephone: 01229 466086   OS Ref: SD238751   Operator: D. Gill
Line length: 180yd, end to end   First opened: 1995

| No | Name | Type | Builder | Built |
|----|------|------|---------|-------|
| | *Layer* | 4wBE | Pfeifferbahn | 1990 |

## ST ANNES MINIATURE RAILWAY   *10¹/₄in gauge*

Seafront, St Annes, Lancashire
OS Ref: SD322281   Line length: 700yd   First opened: 1973

| No | Name | Type | Builder | Built |
|----|------|------|---------|-------|
| | *St Annes Express* | 4w-4PH | Severn Lamb | 1973 |

This line is more or less rectangular, running through the sand dunes, with the tunnel/stock shed at the back of the circuit.

## THE RAILWAY AGE MINIATURE RAILWAY   *7¹/₄in gauge*

The Railway Age, Vernon Way, Crewe, Cheshire CW1 2DB
Telephone: 01270 212130   OS Ref: SJ709553   Operator: The Railway Age
Line length: 600yd   First opened: 1992

| No | Name | Type | Builder | Built |
|----|------|------|---------|-------|
| 7940 | | 4w-4BE | Severn Lamb | 1987 |
| | *Jenny* | 2-4-0ST | Marsh/Rogers | 1992 |
| D7003 | *Norcliff* | 4w-4PH | ESSE | 1993 |
| | | 0-6-0T | R. Elmore | c1987 |

An unusual line squeezed into the confines of this museum site. Trains leave terminus A, cross over the entrance drive and through a short tunnel to terminus B, where the loco turns and runs round. There is then a straight run between the site perimeter and the prototype Advanced Passenger Train displayed here, to terminus C, adjacent to Crewe North signalbox, where the loco again turns and runs round, before repeating the journey in the opposite direction.

*All ready but awaiting passengers, 2-4-0ST* Jenny *and her train stand in the main 7¼in gauge terminus at the Railway Age, Crewe, on 1 April 1994.*
Simon Townsend

## WINDMILL ANIMAL FARM, 15in GAUGE HERITAGE CENTRE
*15in gauge*

Red Cat Lane, Burscough, Lancashire
Telephone: 01704 892282   OS Ref: SD427156   Operator: A. Moss
Line length: 700yd, end to end   First opened: 1997   Farm entry fee

| No | Name | Type | Builder | Built |
|----|------|------|---------|-------|
| | *Whippit Quick* | 4w-4DM | Lister | 1935 |
| | *St Nicholas* | S/O 2-8-0PH | Severn Lamb | 1978 |
| | *Duke of Edinburgh* | S/O 4-6-2DE | H. Barlow | 1950 |
| | *Blue Pacific* | 4-6-2 | N. Guinness | 1935 |
| No 1 | | S/O 4-6-0DM | Jubilee/Volante | 1987 |

A new line running from the farm to a picnic area at Lakeside. It is intended to construct a museum building adjacent to the terminus here. Rapid progress has been made over the last 12 months in building the line and restoring items of rolling stock; more potential exhibits are stored off site awaiting their turn. Whilst *Blue Pacific* is not operational, a further steam locomotive is expected to arrive shortly.

*Austin Moss gives 4-6-2DE* Duke of Edinburgh *a trial run at Windmill Animal Farm in May 1997.* Dave Holroyde

## FLAMINGOLAND MINIATURE RAILWAY    *15in gauge*

Flamingoland, Kirby Misperton, nr Malton, North Yorkshire YO17 0UX
Telephone: 01653 668287    OS Ref: SE779799    Operator: Flamingoland Ltd
Line length: 600yd, circular.    First opened: *c*1969    Park entry fee

| No | Name | Type | Builder | Built |
|----|------|------|---------|-------|
| 7, 278 | | S/O 2-8-0DH | Severn Lamb | 1984 |

The line is one of many attractions at this leisure park.

*On the Heatherslaw Light Railway, 0-4-2* The Lady Augusta *stands with her train. This locomotive is thought to be unique on 15in gauge, being fitted with disc brakes.*
Robin Butterell

## HEATHERSLAW LIGHT RAILWAY    *15in gauge*

Ford Forge, Heatherslaw, Cornhill-on-Tweed, Northumberland TD12 4QA
Telephone: 01890 820244    OS Ref: NT9343834
Operator: Heatherslaw Light Rly Co Ltd    Line length: 1¾ miles, end to end
First opened: 1989

| No | Name | Type | Builder | Built |
|----|------|------|---------|-------|
| | *The Lady Augusta* | 0-4-2 | B. Taylor | 1989 |
| | *Clive* | 6wDH | N. Smith | 1989 |

Neville Smith's railway runs from the Old Forge along the banks of the River Till past fields and woodland to terminate below the ruins of Etal Castle. Trains depart hourly, and are normally steam-hauled, from Easter to the end of October (closed Fridays in October).

## HEMSWORTH WATER PARK MINIATURE RAILWAY  *7¹/₄in gauge* ◼

Hemsworth Water Park, Wakefield Road, Kinsley, nr Hemsworth,
West Yorkshire
Telephone: 01977 617617   OS Ref: SE421147   Operator: N Bartle
Line length: 300yd, circular   First opened: 1993   Park entry fee

| No | Name | Type | Builder | Built |
|----|------|------|---------|-------|
| | *Christopher* | S/O 4w-2PH | J. Horsfield | 1990 |
| | *Lucy* | 0-4-2T | J. Stubbs | 1991 |

This line has one station, with a spur
to a turntable and three-road shed. A

trip is two circuits.

## KIRKLEES LIGHT RAILWAY  *15in gauge* ▬▬▬▬▬▬▬

Park Mill Way, Long Lane, Clayton West, West Yorkshire HD8 9XJ
Telephone: 01484 865727   OS Ref: SE258112
Operator: Kirklees Light Rly Co Ltd   Line length: 3¹/₂ miles, end to end
First opened: 1991

| No | Name | Type | Builder | Built |
|----|------|------|---------|-------|
| | *Fox* | 2-6-2T | B. Taylor | 1987 |
| | *Badger* | 0-6-4ST | B. Taylor | 1991 |
| | | 2-2wPH | B. Taylor | 1991 |
| | *Jay* | 4wDH | B. Taylor | 1992 |
| | *Hawk* | 0-4-0+0-4-0 | B. Taylor | 1998 |

This line has been built to re-create
the atmosphere of a fussy little branch
line. Running from Clayton West along
the embankment of a standard gauge
trackbed, the railway has recently been
extended for a further two miles to
Shelley, the journey now including a

¹/₄-mile tunnel. A new station building
has also been constructed and a Kitson
Meyer articulated locomotive is now
completed. Trains run hourly from
11am on weekends and bank/public
holidays all year round, and daily from
Whitsun to the end of August.

*Brian Taylor's particular brand of 15in gauge design is well illustrated in this photograph of
0-6-4ST* Badger *and train, at the Kirklees Light Railway, on 9 April 1994.*
Simon Townsend

# LAKESHORE RAILROAD *9¹/₂in gauge*

South Marine Park, South Shields, Tyne & Wear
OS Ref: NZ373674  Operators: D. Proudlock & M. Henderson
Line length: 550yd, circular  First opened: 1972

| No | Name | Type | Builder | Built |
|---|---|---|---|---|
| 3440 | *Mountaineer* | 4-6-2 | Jennings/Proudlock/Wakefield | 1968 |
| 27 | *Adiela* | 2-6-2 | Bell/Burgoyne | c1939 |
| | | | reb Proudlock/Henderson | 1976 |

This line runs around the lake in this public park, with numerous footpath crossings. Both locos are notable scale models, *Mountaineer* being ¹/₆ scale of an Atchison, Topeka & Santa Fe prototype, and *Adiela* a ¹/₄ scale of a Ferrcarril National del Magdalena (Colombia) locomotive.

*A special weekday train for the photographer pauses at the station, hauled by 4-6-2 Mountaineer, at the 9¹/₂in gauge Lakeshore Railroad at South Shields. Robin Butterell*

# LAKESIDE RAILWAY *10¹/₄in gauge*

Roundhay Park, Roundhay, Leeds, West Yorkshire
OS Ref: SE331384  Operator: H. Kershaw  Line length: 600yd, dumb-bell
First opened: 1989

| No | Name | Type | Builder | Built |
|---|---|---|---|---|
| | | 4wPM | Clitheroe/Stanhope/Kershaw | 1987 |

A line with rustic charm, running through trees adjacent to the lake at the north end of this large public park.

## LIGHTWATER VALLEY MINIATURE RAILWAY  *15in gauge*

Lightwater Valley Theme Park, North Stainley, nr Ripon,
North Yorkshire HG4 3HT
Telephone: 01765 635321   OS Ref: SE285756
Operator: Lightwater Leisure Ltd   Line length: 1,300yd, circular
First opened: 1979

| No | Name | Type | Builder | Built |
|----|------|------|---------|-------|
| 7, 278 | | S/O 2-8-0DH | Severn Lamb | 1979 |
| | *Little Giant* | 4-4-2 | Bassett Lowke | 1905 |
| 111 | *Yvette* | 4-4-0 | E. Craven | 1946 |

A well engineered line carrying visitors from one side of the park to the other. The two steam locomotives are privately owned and are steamed here occasionally; at other times they can be found within the spacious olde worlde engine shed.

*The driver checks the locomotive in the arrival platform at the Lightwater Valley Railway.*
Robin Butterell

## METAL BRIDGE RAILWAY  *7¹⁄₄in gauge*

The Poachers Pocket Public House, Metal Bridge, nr Ferryhill,
County Durham
Telephone: 01740 654268   OS Ref: NZ300351   Line length: 200yd, circular
First opened: 1994

| No | Name | Type | Builder | Built |
|----|------|------|---------|-------|
| 0123 | *Princess Claire* | 4wBE | Harvey/Maxitrak | 1990 |

*A sunny spring day in May 1992 brought the crowds out to Newby Hall, for a ride behind 10¹/₄in gauge 4-6-0 Royal Scot. Simon Townsend*

## NEWBY HALL MINIATURE RAILWAY   *10¹/₄in gauge*

Newby Hall Gardens, Skelton on Ure, nr Ripon, North Yorkshire HG4 5AE
Telephone: 01423 322583   OS Ref: SE347675   Operator: Hon R. Compton
Line length: 1,000yd, dumb-bell   First opened: 1971

| No | Name | Type | Builder | Built |
|----|------|------|---------|-------|
| 6100 | *Royal Scot* | 4-6-0 | S. Battison | 1953 |
| | *Countess de Grey* | 4w-4PH | Severn Lamb | 1973 |

This line has an attracive little station more or less in the middle of the track. Trains run parallel to the River Ure before reaching the first loop which includes a tunnel. On the return journey trains run through the station non-stop, before crossing a bridge and entering the second loop which passes through a wood.

## NORTH BAY RAILWAY   *20in gauge*

Northstead Manor Gardens, Scarborough, North Yorkshire
OS Ref: TA035898   Operator: Scarborough Borough Council
Line length: 1,300yd, end to end   First opened: 1931

| No | Name | Type | Builder | Built |
|----|------|------|---------|-------|
| 1931 | *Neptune* | S/O 4-6-2DH | Hudswell Clarke | 1931 |
| 1932 | *Triton* | S/O 4-6-2DH | Hudswell Clarke | 1932 |

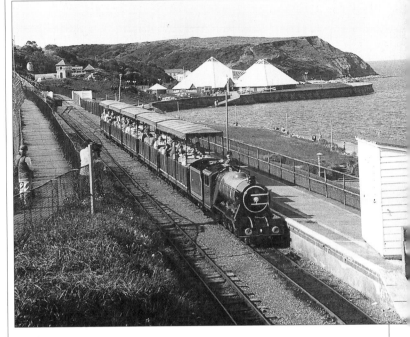

*A panoramic view of the bay at Scarborough for the passengers returning from Scalby Mills, hauled by 4-6-2DH Neptune on 6 May 1992.* Simon Townsend

Trains depart from Peasholm station, dive beneath the water chute and through a short tunnel before swinging out to gain the seafront at the half-way passing loop, whence they continue to Scalby Mills. There is now a turntable at Scalby Mills, but at Peasholm locomotives run round and turn by means of a sharply curved loop. A professionally run line performing a useful task in transporting visitors to and from the attractions at Scalby Mills.

## ORCHARD FARM LAKESIDE RAILWAY  *10¹/₄in gauge*

Orchard Farm Holiday Village, Hunmanby, North Yorkshire YO14 0PU
Telephone: 01723 891582   OS Ref: TA104778   Operator: A Hunneybell
Line length: 500yd, dumb-bell   First opened: 1995

| No | Name | Type | Builder | Built |
|----|------|------|---------|-------|
| | *Honeywell* | 4w-4DH | A. Hunneybell/IBC Welding | 1992 |
| 6100 | *Royal Scot* | 4-6-0 | J. Leach | c1975 |
| | *Sir Walter Gower* | 4-4-2 | Gower/Boughton | c1970 |

A recently constructed line in the grrounds of a caravan park. It boasts an attractive station with overall roof, from where trains head out and around the lake. *Honeywell*, an HST look-alike, is the usual motive power.

73

*4w-4DH* Honeywell *stands beneath the station canopy at the Orchard Farm Lakeside Railway.*
Dave Holroyde

## RIO GRANDE EXPRESS  10¹/₄in gauge

Saville Bros Garden Centre, Garforth Cliff, Garforth, West Yorkshire
OS Ref: SE416319   Operator Saville Bros Ltd   Line length: 900yd, dumb bell
First opened: 1978

| No | Name | Type | Builder | Built |
|----|------|------|---------|-------|
| 278 |  | S/O 2-8-0PH | Severn Lamb | 1978 |

## RUSWARP MINIATURE RAILWAY  7¹/₄in gauge

The Carrs, Ruswarp, nr Whitby, North Yorkshire
OS Ref: NZ885088   Operator: D. Sims   Line length: 700yd, circular
First opened: 1990

| No | Name | Type | Builder | Built |
|----|------|------|---------|-------|
|  | *Danny* | 2-4-2 | D. & G. Sims | 1992 |
|  | *Emily* | 2-4-2T | D. & G. Sims | 1994 |

This line is a convoluted circuit, twisted round upon itself on land adjacent to the River Esk. Both the locos were built by Doug Sims and are minium gauge types, *Emily* being sit-in.

## SALTBURN MINIATURE RAILWAY  15in gauge

Cat Nab, Saltburn, Redcar & Cleveland
OS Ref: NZ667216   Operator: Saltburn Min Rly Assoc.
Line length: 700yd, end to end   First opened: 1947

| No | Name | Type | Builder | Built |
|----|------|------|---------|-------|
|  | *Prince Charles* | S/O 4-6-2DE | H. Barlow | 1953 |
|  | *George Outhwaite* | S/O 0-4-0DH | Saltburn Min Rly Assoc | 1993 |

A long-established line running from a coastal terminus at Cat Nab into the Jubilee Gardens. Its future now seems assured since it was taken over by a group of enthusiasts some years ago.

## SHIBDEN MINIATURE RAILWAY  *10¹/₄in gauge*

Shibden Park, Listers Road, Halifax, West Yorkshire HX3 6XG
Telephone: 01422 367268   OS Ref: SE108262   Operator: K. Norris
Line length: 700yd, circular   First opened: 1983

| No | Name | Type | Builder | Built |
|----|------|------|---------|-------|
| No 1 | *Ivor* | 0-6-0ST | B. Taylor | 1984 |
| | *Ivan* | 4w-4wDE | B. Taylor | 1985 |

This railway is situated at the valley bottom of a large park that includes a museum in Shibden Hall. The track loops around between a stream and the side of the valley through woodland and a picnic area. There is a tunnel and two bridges over the stream.

*0-6-0ST* Ivor *hauls a train around a sharp curve at the Shibden Miniature Railway, Halifax.*

## SOUTH GARDEN MINIATURE RAILWAY  *7¹/₄in gauge*

National Railway Museum, Leeman Road, York YO2 4XJ
Telephone: 01904 621261   OS Ref: SE593519
Operator: National Railway Museum   Line length: 200yd, end to end
First opened: 1996

| No | Name | Type | Builder | Built |
|----|------|------|---------|-------|
| | *John* | 6wPH | R. Greatrex | 1997 |
| | | 6wPH | R. Greatrex | 1998 |
| | | 4wPH | Maxitrak | 1991 |
| | *Taw* | 2-6-2T | Milner Engineering | 1980 |
| | *Margaret* | 0-4-0ST | National Railway Museum | 1981 |
| | *Lashin' Middlin* | 0-4-0ST | R. Gibbon | 1987 |

This modest line has been laid in the South Yard of the National Railway Museum; out and back with a station at the middle of the run. Some of the above locomotives may at times be displayed among the other large scale models within the museum.

## THORNES PARK RAILWAY  *7¹/₄in gauge*

Thornes Park, Horbury Road, Wakefield, West Yorkshire
OS Ref: SE323200   Operator: Wakefield Society of Model & Experimental
Engineers   Line length: 800yd, circular   First opened: c1974

| No | Name | Type | Builder | Built |
|----|------|------|---------|-------|
|  | New York Central | 4-8-4 | J. Stubbs | 1988 |
|  | Linda | 0-4-0ST | J. Stubbs | 1978 |
|  | Bluebell | 0-4-2T | J. Stubbs | 1993 |
| 12 | Alice | 2-4-2 | J. Stubbs | 1995 |
| 13 | Hiawatha | 4-6-4 | J. Stubbs/I. Hickling | 1997 |
| 517 |  | 6w-6wPH | Stubbs/Phillips | 1986 |
| 70008 | Black Prince | 4-6-2 | A. Bickerstaffe | 1989 |
|  | Edward | 0-4-0WT | A. Bennett | 1986 |
| 4082 |  | 0-6-0T |  |  |
| 14 | Petunia | 0-4-2T | Stubbs/Hurley | 1997 |
|  |  | 0-4-0ST | K. Sabey | 1996 |
|  | Ken Rosewarne | 4-4-0 | Leeds Grammar School | c1971 |

This line is a circle wrapped across itself, by means of a diamond crossing. It has an impressive stable of motive power. Trains run every Sunday afternoon.

*This fine 4-6-4 was built by Jeff Stubbs and Ian Hickling in eight months, to a Henry Greenly design. Here the locomotive runs its first trials, on the Thornes Park Railway at Wakefield, in February 1997.* Neville Knight

## WHORLTON LIDO RAILWAY  *15in gauge*

Whorlton Lido, Whorlton, nr Barnard Castle, County Durham
Telephone: 01833 627397   OS Ref: NZ106146   Operator: Mrs Watson
Line length: 700yd, dumb-bell   First opened: 1971

| No | Name | Type | Builder | Built |
|----|------|------|---------|-------|
|  | Wendy | 4-4wDM | R. Dunn/Coleby Simkins | 1972 |

Whorlton Lido is a popular beauty spot, the line was built when it was owned by the Dunn family. Its steam locos have now gone elsewhere, but *Wendy* still operates here.

## AGNEW PARK MINIATURE RAILWAY   7¹/₄in gauge

Agnew Park, Seafront, Stranraer, Wigtownshire
Telephone: 01776 702151 ext 61345   OS Ref: NX056612
Operator: Dumfries and Galloway Council   Line length: 900yd, circular
First opened: 1997

| No | Name | Type | Builder | Built |
|----|------|------|---------|-------|
|    | *Princess Victoria* | 6wPH | R. Greatrex | 1997 |

The railway follows contours around the boating lake and childrens' playground with a station adjacent to the Agnew Park Pavilion. There are extensive sea views down Loch Ryan to Ailsa Craig and Arran.

## AYR MINIATURE RAILWAY   10¹/₄in gauge

Peter Pan Playground, The Promenade, Ayr, South Ayrshire
OS Ref: NS332221   Operator: South Ayrshire District Council
Line length: 250yd, circular   First opened: 1968

| No | Name | Type | Builder | Built |
|----|------|------|---------|-------|
|    | *Ayr Princess* | 6w-6PH | Severn Lamb | 1968 |

A Severn Lamb 'Western' class operates on this short line.

## BRECHIN CASTLE CENTRE RAILWAY   10¹/₄in gauge

Brechin Castle Garden Centre, Haughmuir, Brechin, Angus DD9 6RL
Telephone: 01356 626813   OS Ref: NO577600   Operator: Lord Ramsay
Line length: 300yd, circular   First opened: 1997

| No | Name | Type | Builder | Built |
|----|------|------|---------|-------|
|    |      | 4-4wPH | A. Binning | 1988 |

## CRAIGTOUN MINIATURE RAILWAY   15in gauge

Craigtoun Park, St Andrews, Fife
OS Ref: NO482141   Operator: Fife Council
Line length: 400yd, circular   First opened: *c*1960

| No | Name | Type | Builder | Built |
|----|------|------|---------|-------|
| 278 | *Ivor* | S/O 2-8-0DH | Severn Lamb | 1976 |

This railway was altered in 1995/6 from an end-to-end line to a circuit around the lake.

# KERR'S MINIATURE RAILWAY  *10¹/₄in gauge*

West Links Park, Arbroath, Angus
Telephone: 01241 879249   OS Ref: NO629401   Operator: M. Kerr
Line length: 400yd, end to end   First opened: 1935

| No | Name | Type | Builder | Built |
|---|---|---|---|---|
| 9872 | *Auld Reekie* | S/O 4-4-2PM | W. Jennings | 1935 |
| 2005 | *King George VI* | 4-6-2 | H. Bullock | 1935 |
| 25081 | | 4-4wPM | M. Eastwood | 1981 |
| | *Ivor* | 0-6-0PM | Coleby Simkins | 1972 |
| 3007 | *Firefly* | 0-6-0 | H. Bullock | 1936 |
| D7594 | | 4-4wPM | M. Eastwood | 1992 |
| | *Tich* | 0-4-0T | D. Watt | 1994 |

*From the footbridge we get a panoramic view of the station layout on Kerrs Miniature Railway on a sunny day in August 1994. 0-6-0 Firefly coasts into the station, whilst veteran 4-4-2PM Auld Reekie stands in Platform 1. Matthew Kerr*

'KMR' is one of Britain's oldest miniature railways, having carried over 1¹/₄ million passengers. It runs there and back adjacent to ScotRail's main line between Aberdeen and Edinburgh, passing through a tunnel as it goes. Matthew and his team of volunteers maintain the line in immaculate condition, its straight track renowned for not having a stone of ballast out of place. Saturdays are favourite for steam operation. Children's rides are also given in a miniature bus and fire engine when the railway is open.

## MULL & WEST HIGHLAND NARROW GAUGE RAILWAY
*10¹/₄in gauge*

Craignure, Isle of Mull, Argyll & Bute PA65 6AY
Telephone: 01680 812494   OS Ref: NM724369
Operator: Mull & West Highland Narrow Gauge Rly Co Ltd
Line length: 1¹/₂ miles, end to end   First opened: 1993

| No | Name | Type | Builder | Built |
|----|------|------|---------|-------|
| 196 | *Waverley* | 4-4-2 | D. Curwen | 1948 |
| 5330 | | 4-4wPM | A. Allcock | 1973 |
| | *Lady of the Isles* | 2-6-4T | R. Marsh | 1981 |
| | *Glen Auldyn* | 4w-4wDH | R. Davies | 1986 |
| | *Victoria* | 2-6-2T | D. Vere | 1993 |

*2-6-2T* Victoria *stands at Craignure on the Mull & West Highland Narrow Gauge Railway.*
*MV* Isle of Mull *departs en route for Oban, in the background.*

Trains run from the station at Craignure Old Pier, near to the terminal of the ferry from Oban, to Torosay Castle and gardens. *En route* to the passing loop at Tarmstedt can be seen panoramic views of Ben Nevis, the Glencoe hills, the island of Lismore and Duart Castle. The line then enters a more heavily graded section through woodland. This 'minimum gauge' line is Scotland's only island passenger railway.

## NESS ISLANDS RAILWAY   *7¹/₄in gauge*

Whin Island, Bught Park, Inverness, Highland
OS Ref: NH655433   Operator: I. Young   Line length: 800yd, dumb-bell
First opened: 1983

| No | Name | Type | Builder | Built |
|----|------|------|---------|-------|
| 47548 | *Uncle Frank* | 6w-6wDH | Mardyke | 1989 |
| D7071 | *Uncle Louis* | 4w-4wDH | Mardyke | 1990 |
| | *Uncle John* | 0-4-2T | R. Marsh | 1978 |

Britain's most northerly public miniature railway is situated on the Western edge of Inverness, on an island consisting mainly of a children's play park and boating lake. The line is a dumb-bell folded over on top of itself, with the station on the 'C'-shaped single line in the middle. The steam loco normally operates at weekends.

## ABERAERON WILDLIFE AND LEISURE PARK RAILWAY ▬▬▬
*7¹/₄in gauge*

Aberaeron Wildlife and Leisure Park, Blaen y Waun, Aberaeron,
Cardiganshire FA46 0LA
Telephone: 01545 570766   OS Ref: SN481622   Line length: 550yd
First opened: 1990   Park entry fee

| No | Name | Type | Builder | Built |
|----|------|------|---------|-------|
| | *Sir Geraint Evans* | 0-4-0ST | J. Horsfield | 1989 |
| | | 4-4wPH | Pfeifferbahn | 1979 |
| | | 4wPH | Pfeifferbahn | 1984 |

## CONWY VALLEY RAILWAY   *7¹/₄in and also 15in gauge* ▬▬▬

Conwy Valley Railway Museum, Old Station, Betws-y-Coed, Conwy LL24 0AL
Telephone: 01690 710568   OS Ref: SH796565   Operator: C. Cartwright
7¹/₄in gauge, 950yd   First opened: 1979
15in gauge, 500yd, end to end   First opened: 1991

| No | Name | Type | Builder | Built |
|----|------|------|---------|-------|
| *7¹/₄in gauge:* | | | | |
| D7000 | | 4w-4PM | T. Smith | 1967 |
| 407 | *Old Rube* | 2-8-0 | Milner Engineering | 1983 |
| 6201 | *Princess Elizabeth* | 4-6-2 | D. & A. Barton | c1959 |
| 6641 | | 4-4wPH | R. Greatrex | 1990 |
| 402 | *Shoshone* | 2-8-0 | Milner Engineering | 1977 |
| | *Siân* | 0-4-2T | K. Humphreys | 1988 |
| 403 | *Prince of the Parsenn* | 0-6-0+0-6-0BE | Pfeifferbahn | 1987 |
| 7 | | S/O 4wBER | Parkside | 1995 |
| *15in gauge:* | | | | |
| | | 4w-4wWER | Wall/Cartwright | 1989 |
| 70000 | *Britannia* | 4-6-2 | Longfleet/TMA | 1988 |

The Conwy Valley Railway Museum can be found over the footbridge from Betws-y-coed station. Within the museum can be found the fine scale model of *Britannia*, along with exhibits including other large scale models. Outside the museum is an extensive and ever-popular 7¹/₄in gauge railway, basically a dumb-bell layout with the two loops interlaced. The line crosses behind the museum, protected by automatic level crossing barriers. The 15in gauge line (which crosses over the 7¹/₄in gauge at one point) is worked by an open tram, taking power from an overhead power line using a traditional trolley pole. The 4wBER operates on a separate track put a coin in the slot and drive your own train. The museum, 7¹/₄in gauge line and tramway are complementary attractions, all in a popular location.

*Railways of three gauges are apparent here at Betws-y-coed. On the left is the standard gauge branch line to Blaenau Ffestiniog, next the 15in gauge tramway, and then the 7¹/₄in gauge line, with Nos 407* Old Rube, *and 402* Shoshone *double heading, on 3 October 1993.* Simon Townsend

## FAIRBOURNE & BARMOUTH RAILWAY   12¹/₄in gauge

Beach Road, Fairbourne, Merionethshire LL38 2PZ
Telephone: 01341 250362   OS Ref: SH616128   Operator: North Wales Coast
Light Railway Ltd   Line length: 2 miles, end to end   First opened: 1916

| No | Name | Type | Builder | Built |
|----|------|------|---------|-------|
| 4 | *Sherpa* | 0-4-0ST | Milner Engineering | 1978 |
| E759 | *Yeo* | 2-6-2T | D. Curwen | 1978 |
| 5 | *Russell* | 2-6-4T | Milner Engineering | 1979 |
| 2 | *Beddgelert* | 0-6-4T | D. Curwen | 1979 |
| 6 | *Lilian Walter* | 4w-4wDM | G&SLE | 1961 |
| 7 | *Gwril* | 4wBE | Fairbourne | 1987 |

This line originated in 1896 as a 2ft gauge horse tramway. In 1916 the tramway was relaid to 15in gauge. In this form the line eked out a humble existence until the mid-1950s when a decade of improvements commenced. In 1984 a new owner took over and the line was progressively transformed, including regauging to 12¹/₄in in 1986.

Trains are now mostly hauled by one of four half-size replicas of 2ft gauge steam locomotives, which make a pleasing sight with the distinctive rakes of red coaches. The present owners bought the railway in 1995.

The line runs from Fairbourne station alongside Beach Road and through the sand dunes passing the

*2-6-4T Russell heads a special non-stop train around the loop at Porth Penrhyn, during the Fairbourne & Barmouth Railway's gala weekend in September 1997.* Simon Townsend

station at Gorsafawddachaidraigodan-heddogleddollonpenrhynareurdraeth-ceredigion, formerly named Golf Halt. Trains often pass at the midway loop, before continuing next to the road, then entering a long tunnel and emerging on the far side of the dunes, finally swinging round into Porth Penrhyn. From here it is only a short ferry ride to Barmouth.

## LLWYFAN CERRIG MINIATURE RAILWAY   *7¹/₄in gauge*

Llwyfan Cerrig Station, Gwili Railway, nr Carmarthen,
Carmarthenshire  SA32 6HT
Telephone: 01267 230666   OS Ref: SN405258   Operator: F Bond
Line length: 200yd, end to end   First opened: 1993

| No | Name | Type | Builder | Built |
|----|------|------|---------|-------|
| | *Jason* | 0-4-0T | Page Engineering | 1992 |
| | *Michael* | 0-4-0PH | Page Engineering | 1992 |
| | *Ddraig Ddu* | 0-4-0VBT | R. Harrison | c1978 |

The only public access to this line is by train, on the Gwili Railway from Bronwydd Arms station; the 7¹/₄in gauge line operates on every day that Gwili trains are timetabled. *Jason* and *Michael* both ran at the Welsh National Garden Festival in 1992 before the line here was built.

## OAKWOOD MINIATURE RAILWAY  *15in gauge*

Oakwood Adventure Park, Canaston Bridge, Narberth,
Pembrokeshire SA67 8DE
Telephone: 01834 85373   OS Ref: SN072124   Operator: Oakwood Leisure Ltd
Line length: 1,100yd   First opened: 1987

| No | Name | Type | Builder | Built |
|----|------|------|---------|-------|
| | *Lindy-Lou* | S/O 2-8-0DH | Severn Lamb | 1972 |
| | *Lenka* | 4w-4DHR | Severn Lamb | 1973 |
| 278 | | S/O 2-8-0PH | Severn Lamb | 1976 |
| | *Lorna* | 4-4wDHR | Goold Bros | 1989 |

## RHYL MINIATURE RAILWAY  *15in gauge*

Marine Lake Leisure Park, Wellington Road, Rhyl, Denbighshire
Telephone (E): 01352 759109   OS Ref: SH999807 Operator: L. Hughes
Line length: 1,700yd, circular   First opened: 1911

| No | Name | Type | Builder | Built |
|----|------|------|---------|-------|
| 101 | *Joan* | 4-4-2 | Albert Barnes | 1920 |
| | *Clara* | S/O 0-4-2DM | G&SLE | 1961 |
| KD1 | | 4-4w-4-4w-4DER | Rapido Rail | 1983 |

This line shares (with the Lakeside Miniature Railway, Southport) the honour of running on Britain's oldest miniature railway site. The original railway here closed in 1969, but was relaid in 1978 and then again in 1998. *Joan* operates, weather permitting, on Sundays from Whit to early September, and on peak Thursdays; on these occasions the ride round the Marine Lake is just as you would have found it in 1920. Two further Barnes Atlantics, *Railway Queen* and *Michael*, are also owned by Les Hughes but are presently on display at James Pringle Weavers, Llanfair PG, Anglesey.

*Barnes Atlantic,* Joan, *ready to depart with another train on the Rhyl Miniature Railway, in August 1997.* Simon Townsend

## BELFAST AND COUNTY DOWN MINIATURE RAILWAY  *7¹/₄in gauge*

Upper Gransha Road, Donaghadee, County Down
Telephone (E): 01247 882013   OS Ref: J547761
Operator: Belfast & County Down Miniature Railway Society
Line length: 1,100yd   First opened: 1994

| No | Name | Type | Builder | Built |
|----|------|------|---------|-------|
| 25 | *Winifred* | 0-4-0ST | D. Tedford | 1989 |
| 6 | *Waldenburg* | 0-6-0T | L. Nelson | 1981 |
| | *Finn McCool* | 0-4-2 | TMA Engineering | 1986 |
| | | 0-4-0ST | | |
| | | 6wPH | Greatrex/Tedford | 1998 |

*A busy scene at Drumawhey Junction in August 1997.* David Tedford

The line comprises a circuit off which there is an additional loop. There is one station at Drumawhey Junction, a tunnel and a rail-over-rail bridge.

## COLERAINE & DISTRICT SOCIETY OF MODEL ENGINEERS
*7¹/₄in gauge*

Turnakibbock, Damhead, Coleraine, County Londonderry
OS Ref: C895303   Operator: Coleraine & District
Society of Model Engineers Ltd   Line length: 170yd, circular

| No | Name | Type | Builder | Built |
|----|------|------|---------|-------|
| | *Hercules* | 0-4-2T | T. Snoxell | c1972 |
| | | 0-4-2T | R. Morrison | 1978 |
| 4 | *Hydraulic* | 0-6-0PH | K. Boyd | 1992 |
| | | 0-4-2T | R. Morrison | c1985 |
| | | 0-4-2T | R. Morrison | c1989 |

## CULTRA LIGHT RAILWAY  *7¹/₄in gauge*

Ulster Folk and Transport Museum, Cultra, near Holywood,
County Down BT18 0EU
Telephone: 01232 428428   OS Ref: J418809   Operator: Model Engineers
Society of Northern Ireland   Line length: 360yd, circular   First opened: 1985

| No | Name | Type | Builder | Built |
|----|------|------|---------|-------|
| D7016 |  | 4w-4PM | Cromar White | 1969 |
|  | *Taurus* | 0-4-2T | T. Snoxell | 1984 |
|  | *Wavin (NI) Ltd* | 0-6-0PH | R. Greatrex | 1991 |
|  | *Betty* | 0-4-0ST | MESNI | c1993 |
|  | *Marian* | 0-4-0ST | J. Conn |  |
|  |  | 4wPM | T. D. Wilson | 1984 |

The line here runs in and out of a walled garden. The station at Cultra Central has footbridge access to the elevated 3¹/₂in/5in gauge tracks inside the circuit.

## JOHN F. KENNEDY ARBORETUM MINIATURE RAILWAY
*7¹/₄in gauge*

John F. Kennedy Arboretum, New Ross, nr Canpile, County Wexford
Telephone: 00353 51 88195   OS Ref: S725184
Operator: J. F. Kennedy Arboretum   Line length: 400yd, circular
First opened: 1990

| No | Name | Type | Builder | Built |
|----|------|------|---------|-------|
|  | *Santa Fe* | 4-4wPH | B. Meyler | 1989 |

## LEISURELAND EXPRESS  *15in gauge*

Seafront, Salthill, Galway, Co. Galway
OS Ref: M282240   Operator: Galway Corporation   Line length: 350yd, circular
First opened: 1973

| No | Name | Type | Builder | Built |
|----|------|------|---------|-------|
|  |  | S/O 2-8-0DH | Severn Lamb | 1973 |

The line runs around the amusement park on the sea front, and sometimes runs well into the evenings.

## PICKIE FAMILY FUN PARK RAILWAY  *7¹/₄in gauge*

Pickie Family Fun Park, Seafront, Bangor, County Down
OS Ref: J501820   Operator: North Down Borough Council
Line length: 300yd, balloon   First opened: 1993

| No | Name | Type | Builder | Built |
|----|------|------|---------|-------|
| 1993 | *Pickie Puffer* | S/O 2-4-2DH | Severn Lamb | 1993 |

The line is a balloon loop with one central station and a halt at the opposite end where there is a turning wye.

## TRAMORE MINIATURE RAILWAY *15in gauge*

Fun Park, Seafront, Tramore, County Waterford
OS Ref: S585012   Operator: Tramore Failte Ltd   Line length: 400yd, circular
First opened: 1973

| No | Name | Type | Builder | Built |
|----|------|------|---------|-------|
|    |      | S/O 2-8-0PH | Severn Lamb | 1973 |

This line runs round a fun park, including a boating lake. There are two tunnel/sheds in which the stock is housed at night. During the season, operation often continues into the evenings.

## WESTPORT HOUSE EXPRESS *15in gauge*

Westport House and Children's Zoo, Westport, nr Knock, County Mayo
Telephone: 00353 98 27766   OS Ref: L988845   Operator: Lord Altamont
Line length: 700yd, balloon   First opened: 1990

| No | Name | Type | Builder | Built |
|----|------|------|---------|-------|
|    | *W. H.* | S/O 2-6-0DH | Severn Lamb | 1989 |

*Severn Lamb 2-8-0* W H *heads the Westport House Express on 12 August 1996.*
Dave Holroyde

## ALDERNEY MINIATURE RAILWAY  *7¹/₄in gauge*

Mannez Quarry, Alderney
Telephone: 01481 822941   OS Ref: WA601087   Operator: Alderney Care Trust
Line length: 400yd, circular   First opened: 1995

| No | Name | Type | Builder | Built |
|----|------|------|---------|-------|
| D7029 | | 4w-4PM | Cromar White | 1972 |
| D872 | *HMS Alderney* | 4-4wPH | Curwen & Newbery | c1960 |

*7¹/₄in Gauge Society Chairman Eric Doyle tests his Cromar White 'Hymek' No D7029, on the Alderney Miniature Railway.* Mike Taylor

The railway follows a scenic route in Mannez Quarry, next to the lighthouse. Operation, at weekends, coincides with the standard gauge trains of the Alderney Railway, from Braye Road.

## SAUSMAREZ MANOR MINIATURE RAILWAY  *7¹/₄in gauge*

Sausmarez Manor, Sausmarez Road, St Martins, Guernsey
Telephone: 01481 35571   OS Ref: WV329762   Line length: 400yd, circular
First opened: 1985   House entry fee

| No | Name | Type | Builder | Built |
|----|------|------|---------|-------|
| 1 | *Romulus* | 0-4-0WT | T. Leigh | 1987 |
| | *Remus* | 4-4wPH | T. Leigh | 1989 |

## PUGNEYS LIGHT RAILWAY  *7¹/₄in gauge*

Pugneys Country Park, Durkar, nr Wakefield, West Yorkshire
Operators: A. Sowden and J. Pinder   Line length: 500yd, end to end

| No | Name | Type | Builder | Built |
|----|------|------|---------|-------|
|    |      | 4-4w-4w-4w-4BER | A. Sowden/J. Pinder | 1996 |

## LOCH FYNE MINIATURE RAILWAY  *10¹/₄in gauge*

John Smith Memorial Gardens, Ardrishaig, Argyll
OS Ref: NM848856   Operator: Loch Fyne Miniature Railway Society
Line length: 300yd, end to end

| No | Name | Type | Builder | Built |
|----|------|------|---------|-------|
| 4472 | *Flying Scotsman* | 4-6-2 | Carland Engineering | 1948 |

## CARNFUNNOCK COUNTRY PARK MINIATURE RAILWAY
*7¹/₄in gauge*

Carnfunnock Country Park, Coast Road, Larne, County Antrim
Telephone: 01574 270541   Operator: P. Johnston   Line length: 600yd

| No | Name | Type | Builder | Built |
|----|------|------|---------|-------|
|    | *Colonel Bogey* | 6wPH | R. Greatrex | 1997 |

# CLUB TRACKS

The following Model Engineering Societies also have 7¹/₄in gauge ground level and elevated tracks which sometimes open to the public. Generally, these operate less regularly than the locations described in the main part of the book.

Bedford Model Engineering Society, Summerfields Fruit Farm, Haynes, Bedford, BEDFORDSHIRE; TL099429.

Pinewood Miniature Railway Society, Pinewood Leisure Centre, Old Wokingham Road, Crowthorne, BERKSHIRE; SU838661.

Milton Keynes Model Engineering Society, Kingfisher Country Club, Deanshanger, BUCKINGHAMSHIRE; SP769390.

Vale of Aylesbury Model Engineering Society, Buckinghamshire Railway Centre, Quainton Road, BUCKINGHAMSHIRE; SP741189.

Cambridge Model Engineering Society, Fulbrooke Road, Newnham, Cambridge, CAMBRIDGESHIRE; TL434572.

Dunhams Wood Light Railway, Rodham Road, March, CAMBRIDGESHIRE; TL443975.

Peterborough Model Engineering Society, Thorpe Hall, Longthorpe, Peterborough, CAMBRIDGESHIRE; TL170986.

Ramsey Miniature Steam Railway Society, Mereside Farm, Ramsey, CAMBRIDGESHIRE.

Carlisle & District Model Engineering Society, Upperby Park, Buchanan Road, Upperby, Carlisle, CUMBRIA; NY406534. Elevated track.

Plymouth Miniature Steam Locomotive Society, Goodwin Park, Pendeen Crescent, Southway, Plymouth, DEVON; SX491607.

Bournemouth & District Society of Model Engineers, Kings Park, Pokesdown, Bournemouth, DORSET; SZ116928. Elevated track.

Stoford Miniature Locomotive Society, Sensible Motoring Centre, Henstridge, DORSET; ST761217.

South Durham Society of Model Engineers, Hurworth Grange Community Centre, Hurworth, CO DURHAM; NZ297101. Elevated track.

Cleveland Association of Model Engineers, Tees Cottage Pumping Station, Darlington, CO DURHAM; NZ258139.

East Sussex Model Engineers (Hastings), Alexandra Park, St Helens Road, Hastings, EAST SUSSEX; TQ807107.

Uckfield Model Railway Club, Bentley Wildfowl & Motor Museum, Halland, Uckfield, EAST SUSSEX; TQ484159.

Canvey Railway & Model Engineering Club, Waterside Farm Sports Centre, Canvey Island, ESSEX; TQ781849.

Chelmsford Society of Model Engineers, Meteor Way, Waterhouse Lane, Chelmsford, ESSEX; TL699066.

Rochford Live Steam Group, Freight House, Bradley Way, Rochford, ESSEX; TQ874904.

Saffron Walden & District Model Engineering Society, Audley End Miniature Railway, Saffron Walden, ESSEX; TL523379. Elevated track.

Chingford & District Model Engineering Club, Ridgeway Park, Chingford, GREATER LONDON; TQ378937.

Harrow & Wembley Society of Model Engineers, Roxbourne Park, Field End Road, Eastcote, GREATER LONDON; TQ118869.

Ilford & West Essex Model Railway Club, Chadwell Heath Stn, Station Road, Chadwell Heath, GREATER LONDON; TQ477877.

Willesden & West London Society of Model Engineers, Roundwood Park, Willesden, GREATER LONDON; TQ222842.

Rochdale Society of Model & Experimental Engineers, Springfield Park, Marland, Rochdale, GREATER MANCHESTER; SD875118. Elevated track.

Southampton Society of Model Engineers Ltd, Riverside Park, Bitterne Park, Southampton, HAMPSHIRE; SU437144.

Elmdon Model Engineering Society, Birmingham and Midland Museum of Transport, Wythall, HEREFORD & WORCESTER; SP072750.

Hereford Society of Model Engineers, Hereford Waterworks Museum, Broomy Hill, Hereford, HEREFORD & WORCESTER; SO496392.

Worcester & District Model Engineering Society, Waverley Street, Cherry Orchard, Worcester, HEREFORD & WORCESTER; SO852533.

Manx Steam & Model Engineering Club, Curraghs Wildlife Park, Ballaugh, ISLE OF MAN; SC367943.

Valley Miniature Railway Society, Ashton Park, Darwen, LANCASHIRE; SD695216.

Leyland Society of Model Engineers, Worden Park, Leyland, LANCASHIRE; SD538209.

Westby Miniature Railway Group, Maple Farm Nursery, Peel Hill Bridge, Blackpool, LANCASHIRE; SD363331.

Leicester Society of Model Engineers Ltd, Abbey Park, Leicester, LEICESTERSHIRE; SK584055.

Lincoln & District Model Engineering Society, North Scarle Sports & Social Club, near Lincoln, LINCOLNSHIRE; SK852668.

Merseyside Live Steam & Model Engineers, Harthill Road, Allerton, Liverpool, MERSEYSIDE; SJ402876.

Barton House Riverside Railway, Hartwell Road, Wroxham, NORFOLK; TG304177.

King's Lynn & District Society of Model Engineers, Lynnsport Leisure Centre, King's Lynn, NORFOLK; TF631211.

Pentney Park Railway, Camping & Caravan Site, Narborough, NORFOLK; TF742141.

Northampton Society of Model Engineers Ltd, Lower Delapre Park, London Road, Northampton, NORTHAMPTONSHIRE; SP756593.

Grimsby & Cleethorpes Model Engineering Society, Waltham Windmill, Waltham, Grimsby, NORTH EAST LINCOLNSHIRE; TA259034.

Sandtoft Miniature Railway, Sandtoft Transport Centre, near Crowle, NORTH LINCOLNSHIRE; SE748082.

Bristol Society of Model & Experimental Engineers, Ashton Court Park, NORTH WEST SOMERSET; ST554729.

Ryedale Society of Model Engineers, The Old School, Gilling East, NORTH YORKSHIRE; SE613770.

Chesterfield & District Model Engineering Society, Papplewick Pumping Station, Ravenshead, NOTTINGHAMSHIRE; SK582521.

Nottingham Society of Model & Experimental Engineers, Nottingham Railway Heritage Centre, Ruddington, NOTTINGHAMSHIRE; SK574322.

City of Oxford Society of Model Engineers, Cutteslowe Park, Cutteslowe, Oxford, OXFORDSHIRE; SP510106.

Yeovil College & District Model Engineering Society, Mudford Recreation Centre, Yeovil, SOMERSET; ST553170.

Rotherham & District Model Engineers Society, Victoria (Rosehill) Park, Rawmarsh, SOUTH YORKSHIRE; SK43X97X.

Sheffield & District Model Engineers, Abbeydale Road South, Dore, Sheffield, SOUTH YORKSHIRE; SK322816.

Wortley Top Forge Model Engineers, Wortley Top Forge, Thurgoland, Stocksbridge, SOUTH YORKSHIRE; SK295999.

Wolverhampton & District Model Engineering Society, Baggeridge Country Park, Wombourne, STAFFORDSHIRE; SO898930.

Teesside Small Gauge Railway Society, Preston Park, Eaglescliffe, STOCKTON ON TEES; NZ429161.

Frimley & Ascot Locomotive Club, Frimley Lodge Park, Sturt Road, Frimley, SURREY; SU891560.

Guildford Model Engineering Society, Stoke Park, London Road, Guildford, SURREY; TQ009508.

Malden & District Society of Model Engineers Ltd, Claygate Lane, Thames Ditton, SURREY; TQ162662.

Woking Miniature Railway Society, Mizens Farm, Chertsey Road, Anthonys, Woking, SURREY; TQ011619.

City of Sunderland Model Engineering Society, Roker Park, Roker, Sunderland; TYNE & WEAR; NZ40X59X. Elevated track.

Echills Wood Railway, National Agricultural Centre, Stoneleigh, WARWICKSHIRE; SP325717.

Rugby Model Engineering Society Ltd, Onley Lane, Rugby, WARWICKSHIRE; SP513727.

Chichester & District Society of Model Engineers Ltd, Bognor Road, Chichester, WEST SUSSEX; SU871047.

Barnsley Society of Model Engineers, Kirklees Light Railway, Clayton West, WEST YORKSHIRE; SE259112. Elevated track.

Bradford Model Engineering Society, Northcliffe Woods, Cliffe Wood Avenue, Shipley, WEST YORKSHIRE; SE142366.

Spenborough Model Engineers Ltd, Royds Park, Dewsbury Road, Cleckheaton, WEST YORKSHIRE; SE200248.

West Riding Small Locomotive Society Ltd, Blackgates House, Tingley, Morley, WEST YORKSHIRE; SE291261.

North Wilts Model Engineering Society, Coate Water Country Park, Swindon, WILTSHIRE; SU179827.

Kirkcaldy Model Engineering Society, Beveridge Park, Kirkcaldy, FIFE; NT269911.

Esk Valley Model Engineering Society, Vogrie Country Park, Newtongrange, MIDLOTHIAN; NT377631.

Rolls-Royce Model Engineering Society, Barshaw Park, Glasgow Road, Paisley, RENFREWSHIRE; NS500642. Elevated track.

Strathaven Model Society, George Allan Park, Glasgow Road, Strathaven, SOUTH LANARKSHIRE; NS700448.

Whitchurch (Cardiff) & District Model Engineering Society, Heath Park, Heath, CARDIFF; ST178799.

Wye Valley Railway Society, The Old Station, Tintern, MONMOUTHSHIRE; SO537006.

Mid Wales Model Engineering Society, The Park, Newtown, POWYS; SO106915.

Dublin Society of Model & Experimental Engineers, Marlay Park, Ballinteer, Dublin, COUNTY DUBLIN; O152261.

## STAPLEFORD MINIATURE RAILWAY  $10^1/_4$in gauge

Stapleford Park, Stapleford, nr Melton Mowbray, Leicestershire
OS Ref: SK813182   Operator: Friends of the Stapleford Miniature Railway
Line length: 1 mile, balloon   First opened: 1958

| No | Name | Type | Builder | Built |
|----|------|------|---------|-------|
| 2943 | *Hampton Court* | 4-6-0 | G&SLE/Twining | 1939 |
| 5565 | *Victoria* | 4-6-0 | Moore/Allcock/Coleby Simkins | 1975 |
| 752 | | 2-8-4 | Coleby Simkins | 1971 |
| 751 | *John H. Gretton* | 4-4-2 | D. Curwen | 1948 |
| D100 | *The White Heron* | 4w-4wPM | Curwen & Newbery | 1962 |
| 4498 | *Sir Nigel Gresley* | 4-6-2 | W. Kirkland | 1967 |
| 3.1192 | | 4-6-2 | N. & D. Simkins | 1995 |
| 6019 | | 4-8-4 | D. Wilks | 1998 |

One of the most outstanding $10^1/_4$in gauge railways in the UK, the original line was constructed by the late Lord Gretton, and connected with two model passenger carrying liners on the lake. After the sale of the house the line was remodelled and is now open to the public only on special days as advertised. In 1998 these will be 20/21 June and 30/31 August.

## STOCKHOLES FARM RAILWAY  $7^1/_4$in gauge

Stockholes Farm, 27 Sandtoft Road, Belton, nr Doncaster, North Lincolnshire DN9 1PH
Telephone (E): 01427 872723   OS Ref: SE766075   Operator: I. Smith
Line length: 1,000yd   First opened: 1988

| No | Name | Type | Builder | Built |
|----|------|------|---------|-------|
| 6233 | *Duchess of Sutherland* | 4-6-2 | H. Powell | 1938 |
| | *Pegasus* | 0-6-0T | A. Jenkins | c1981 |
| D111 | | 4-4wBE | D. Perriton | 1973 |
| 5420 | | 4-6-0 | I. Smith | 1998 |
| 35 | *Holmside* | 0-6-0ST | R. Bairstow | 1990 |
| | *Deltic* | 6w-6wBE | C. Bedloe | |
| 6100 | *Royal Scot* | 4-6-0 | R. Gee | c1985 |
| 7132 | | S/O 4wBE | P. Wood | 1993 |
| | *(Toby)* | S/O 4wBE | D. Billmore | 1993 |
| 6231 | *Duchess of Atholl* | 4-6-2 | Brook Motors | c1949 |
| 2663 | *George the Fifth* | 4-4-0 | Bassett Lowke | c1912 |
| 43924 | | 0-6-0 | R. Gomersal | 1994 |
| 67762 | | 2-6-4T | A. Balmforth | 1951 |

An extensive private railway operated by Ivan Smith with a group of volunteers. Public opening in 1998 wll be 4/25 May, 31 August from 11am .Also 7 November from 3pm.

# SOCIETIES TO JOIN

The following societies particularly cater for those interested in miniature railways:

## Narrow Gauge Railway Society

Annual membership runs from 1 April, subscription currently (1998) £14.50, includes journals *Narrow Gauge News* bi-monthly and *The Narrow Gauge* quarterly. Membership Secretary: Lawson Little, 15 Highfields Drive, Old Bilsthorpe, Newark, Nottinghamshire NG22 8SN.

## 7¹/₄ in Gauge Society

Annual membership runs from 1 February, subscription currently (1998) £15, includes *7¹/₄ Gauge News*, quarterly. Membership Secretary: David Everingham, 115 Tom Lane, Sheffield S10 3PE.

## Branch Line Society

Annual membership runs from 1st May, various subscription rates. *Branch Line News*, published fortnightly, includes a column on Minor Railways. Membership Secretary: Mrs K. E. Noakes, 17 Blakes Terrace, New Malden, Surrey KT3 6ET.

## The Heywood Society Journal

Bi-annual journal devoted to miniature railway subjects. Annual subscription covers the May and October issues each year, currently (1998) £7. Details from: Simon Townsend, 10 Cilnant, Mold, Flintshire CH7 1GG.

*No 6233* Duchess of Sutherland *heads a train on the 7¹/₄in gauge Stockholes Farm Miniature railway on 29 June 1997.*
Dave Holroyde

# INDEX

# For all your transport requirements, visit the Ian Allan Bookshops in Birmingham, Manchester or London.

## BIRMINGHAM

Unit 84
47 Stephenson Street
Birmingham B2 4DH
Tel: 0121 643 2496
Fax: 0121 643 6855

## LONDON

45/46 Lower Marsh
Waterloo
London SE1 7SG
Tel: 0171 401 2100

## MANCHESTER

Unit 5
Piccadilly Station Approach
Manchester M1 2GH
Tel: 0161 237 9840
Fax: 0161 237 9921

*Each shop stocks a comprehensive range of books, magazines, videos, models, badges, postcards, calendars and much more!*

*For the full range of Ian Allan products plus books and videos from specialist publishers large and small - call into an Ian Allan Bookshop TODAY!*

The Ian Allan Bookshops also offer a mail order service - please call for details.

To find out if an Ian Allan Bookshop is opening near you, please telephone: **0161 237 9840.**

IAN ALLAN
Bookshops

Front cover, upper: *Two trains await
passengers at Woodland Central station
on the 7¹/₄in gauge Rode Woodland
Railway.* Dave Holroyde

Front cover, lower: *Two fine models,
Nos 4498* Sir Nigel Gresley *and 3.1192,
double-heading at the 10¹/₄in gauge
Stapleford Miniature Railway on
12 October 1997.* Simon Townsend

Back cover: *Trains crossing at Irton Road
station on the 15in gauge Ravenglass &
Eskdale Railway, hauled by* River Irt
*(arriving) and* Synolda. Robin Butterell